# Interactive Mathematics Program

IMP™

## Integrated High School Mathematics

# All About Alice

Dan Fendel and Diane Resek
with
Lynne Alper and Sherry Fraser

This material is based upon work supported by the National Science Foundation under award number ESI-9255262. Any opinions, findings, and conclusions or recommendations expressed in this publication are those of the authors and do not necessarily reflect the views of the National Science Foundation.



Key Curriculum Press
P.O. Box 2304
Berkeley, California 94702
editorial@keypress.com
http://www.keypress.com

10 9 8 7 6 5 4 3 2    01 00 99 98
ISBN 1-55953-264-5
Printed in the
United States of America

Project Editor
Casey FitzSimons

Editorial Assistant
Jeff Gammon

Production Editor
Caroline Ayres

Art Developer
Jason Luz

Mathematics Review
Rick Marks, Ph.D., Sonoma State University
Rohnert Park, California

Teacher Reviews
Daniel R. Bennett, Kualapuu, Hawaii
Larry Biggers, San Antonio, Texas
Dave Calhoun, Fresno, California
Dwight Fuller, Clovis, California
Daniel S. Johnson, Campbell, California
Brent McClain, Hillsboro, Oregon
Amy C. Roszak, Roseburg, Oregon
Carmen C. Rubino, Lakewood, Colorado
Jean Stilwell, Minneapolis, Minnesota
Wendy Tokumine, Honolulu, Hawaii

Multicultural Reviews
Mary Barnes, M.Sc., University of Melbourne,
Cremorne, New South Wales, Australia
Edward D. Castillo, Ph.D., Sonoma State University,
Rohnert Park, California
Joyla Gregory, B.A., College Preparatory School,
Oakland, California
Genevieve Lau, Ph.D., Skyline College,
San Bruno, California
Beatrice Lumpkin, M.S., Malcolm X College (retired),
Chicago, Illinois
Arthur Ramirez, Ph.D., Sonoma State University,
Rohnert Park, California

Cover and Interior Design
Terry Lockman
Lumina Designworks

Production Manager
Steve Rogers, Luis Shein

Production Coordination
Diana Krevsky, Susan Parini

Technical Graphics
Kristen Garneau, Natalie Hill, Greg Reeves

Illustration
Tom Fowler, Evangelia Philippidis, Sara Swan,
Diane Varner, Martha Weston, April Goodman Willy

Publisher
Steven Rasmussen

Editorial Director
John Bergez

# Acknowledgments

Many people have contributed to the development of the IMP curriculum, including the hundreds of teachers and many thousands of students who used preliminary versions of the materials. Of course, there is no way to thank all of them individually, but the IMP directors want to give some special acknowledgments.

We want to give extraordinary thanks to the following people who played unique roles in the development of the curriculum.

- **Rich Hemphill** suggested the use of the Alice story as a metaphor for exponential growth and designed several of the unit's activities.
- **Matt Bremer** did the initial revision of every unit after its pilot testing. Each unit of the curriculum also underwent extensive focus group reexamination after being taught for several years, and Matt did the rewrite of many units following the focus groups. He has read every word of everyone else's revisions as well and has contributed tremendous insight through his understanding of high school students and the high school classroom.
- **Mary Jo Cittadino** became a high school student once again during the piloting of the curriculum, attending class daily and doing all the class activities, homework, and POWs. Because of this experience, her contributions to focus groups had a unique perspective. This is a good place to thank her also for her contributions to IMP as Network Coordinator for California. In that capacity, she has visited many IMP classrooms and has answered thousands of questions from parents, teachers, and administrators.
- **Lori Green** left the classroom as a regular teacher after the 1989-90 school year and became a traveling resource for IMP classroom teachers. In that role, she has seen more classes using the curriculum than we can count. She has compiled many of the insights from her classroom observations in the *Teaching Handbook for the Interactive Mathematics Program*™.
- **Bill Finzer** was one of the original directors of IMP before going on to different pastures. Though he was not involved in the writing of Year 2, his ideas about curriculum are visible throughout the program.
- **Celia Stevenson** developed the charming and witty graphics that graced the prepublication versions of all the IMP units.

Several people played particular roles in the development of this unit, *All About Alice:*

- Matt Bremer, Janice Bussey, Donna Gaarder, Theresa Hernandez-Heinz, Linda Schroers, and Adrienne Yank helped us create the version of *All About Alice* that was pilot tested during 1990-91. They not only taught the unit in their classrooms that year, but also read and commented on early drafts, tested almost all the activities during workshops that preceded the teaching, and then came back after teaching the unit with insights that contributed to the initial revision.

- Melody Martinez, Robin Rice, and Greg Smith joined Matt Bremer, Mary Jo Cittadino, and Lori Green for the focus group on *All About Alice* in May, 1995. Their contributions built on several years of IMP teaching, including at least two years teaching this unit, and their work led to the development of the last field-test version of the unit.
- Dan Branham, Dave Calhoun, Steve Hansen, Gwennyth Trice, and Julie Walker field tested the post-focus-group version of *All About Alice* during 1995–96. Dave and Gwennyth met with us to share their experiences when the teaching of the unit was finished. Their feedback helped shape the final version that now appears.

In creating this program, we needed help in many areas other than writing curriculum and giving support to teachers.

The National Science Foundation (NSF) has been the primary sponsor of the Interactive Mathematics Program. We want to thank NSF for its ongoing support, and we especially want to extend our personal thanks to Dr. Margaret Cozzens, Director of NSF's Division of Elementary, Secondary, and Informal Education for her encouragement and her faith in our efforts.

We also want to acknowledge here the initial support for curriculum development from the California Postsecondary Education Commission and the San Francisco Foundation, and the major support for dissemination from the Noyce Foundation and the David and Lucile Packard Foundation.

Keeping all of our work going required the help of a first-rate office staff. This group of talented and hard-working individuals worked tirelessly on many tasks, such as sending out units, keeping the books balanced, helping us get our message out to the public, and handling communications with schools, teachers, and administrators. We greatly appreciate their dedication.

- Barbara Ford—Secretary
- Tony Gillies—Project Manager
- Marianne Smith—Communications Manager
- Linda Witnov—Outreach Coordinator

We want to thank Dr. Norman Webb of the Wisconsin Center for Education Research for his leadership in our evaluation program, and our Evaluation Advisory Board, whose expertise was so valuable in that aspect of our work.

- David Clarke, University of Melbourne
- Robert Davis, Rutgers University
- George Hein, Lesley College
- Mark St. John, Inverness Research Associates

## IMP National Advisory Board

We have been further supported in this work by our National Advisory Board—a group of very busy people who found time in their schedules to give us more than a piece of their minds every year. We thank them for their ideas and their forthrightness.

David Blackwell
Professor of Mathematics and Statistics
University of California, Berkeley

Constance Clayton
Professor of Pediatrics
Chief, Division of Community Health Care
Medical College of Pennsylvania

Tom Ferrio
Manager, Professional Calculators
Texas Instruments

Andrew M. Gleason
Hollis Professor of Mathematics and Natural Philosophy
Department of Mathematics
Harvard University

Milton Gordon
President and Professor of Mathematics
California State University, Fullerton

Shirley Hill
Curator's Professor of Education and Mathematics
School of Education
University of Missouri

Steven Leinwand
Mathematics Consultant
Connecticut Department of Education

Art McArdle
Northern California Surveyors Apprentice Committee

Diane Ravitch (1994 only)
Senior Research Scholar
Brookings Institution

Roy Romer (1992-1994 only)
Governor
State of Colorado

Karen Sheingold
Research Director
Educational Testing Service

Theodore R. Sizer
Chairman
Coalition of Essential Schools

Gary D. Watts
Educational Consultant

Finally, we want to thank Steve Rasmussen, President of Key Curriculum Press, Casey FitzSimons, Key's Project Editor for the IMP curriculum, and the many others at Key whose work turned our ideas and words into published form.

Dan Fendel Diane Resek Lynne Alper Sherry Fraser

# Foreword

*Is There Really a Difference?* asks the title of one Year 2 unit of the Interactive Mathematics Program (IMP).

"You bet there is!" As Superintendent of Schools, I have found that IMP students in our District have more fun, are well prepared for our State Testing Program in the tenth grade, and are a more representative mix of the different groups in our geographical area than students in other pre-college math classes. Over the last few years, IMP has become an important example of curriculum reform in both our math and science programs.

When we decided in 1992 to pilot the Interactive Mathematics Program, we were excited about its modern approach to restructuring the traditional high school math sequence of courses and topics and its applied use of significant technology. We hoped that IMP would not only revitalize the pre-college math program, but also extend it to virtually all ninth-grade students. At the same time, we had a few concerns about whether IMP students would acquire all of the traditional course skills in algebra, geometry, and trigonometry.

Within the first year, the program proved successful and we were exceptionally pleased with the students' positive reaction and performance, the feedback from parents, and the enthusiasm of teachers. Our first group of IMP students, who graduated in June, 1996, scored as well on PSATs, SATs, and State tests as a comparable group of students in the traditional program did, and subsequent IMP groups are doing the same. In addition, the students have become our most enthusiastic and effective IMP promoters when visiting middle school classes to describe math course options to incoming ninth graders. One student commented, "IMP is the most fun math class I've ever had." Another said, "IMP makes you work hard, but you don't even notice it."

In our first pilot year, we found that the IMP course reached a broader range of students than the traditional Algebra 1 course did. It worked wonderfully not only for honors students, but for other students who would not have begun algebra study until tenth grade or later. The most successful students were those who became intrigued with exciting applications, enjoyed working in a group, and were willing to tackle the hard work of thinking seriously about math on a daily basis.

IMP Year 2 places the graphing calculator and computer in central positions early in the math curriculum. Students thrive on the regular group collaboration and grow in self-confidence and skill as they present their ideas to a large group. Most importantly, not only do students learn the symbolic and graphing applications of elementary algebra, the statistics of *Is There Really a Difference?,* and the geometry of *Do Bees Build It Best?,* but the concepts have meaning to them.

I wish you well as you continue your IMP path for a second year. I am confident that students and teachers using Year 2 will enjoy mathematics more than ever as they experiment, investigate, and discover solutions to the problems and activities presented this year.

Reginald Mayo

Reginald Mayo
Superintendent
New Haven Public Schools
New Haven, Connecticut

# The Interactive Mathematics Program

## What is the Interactive Mathematics Program?

The Interactive Mathematics Program (IMP) is a growing collaboration of mathematicians, teacher-educators, and teachers who have been working together since 1989 on both curriculum development and professional development for teachers.

## What is the IMP curriculum?

IMP has created a four-year program of problem-based mathematics that replaces the traditional Algebra I–Geometry–Algebra II/Trigonometry–Precalculus sequence and that is designed to exemplify the curriculum reform called for in the *Curriculum and Evaluation Standards* of the National Council of Teachers of Mathematics (NCTM).

The IMP curriculum integrates traditional material with additional topics recommended by the NCTM *Standards,* such as statistics, probability, curve fitting, and matrix algebra. Although every IMP unit has a specific mathematical focus, most units are structured around a central problem and bring in other topics as needed to solve that problem, rather than narrowly restricting the mathematical content. Ideas that are developed in one unit are generally revisited and deepened in one or more later units.

## For which students is the IMP curriculum intended?

The IMP curriculum is for all students. One of IMP's goals is to make the learning of a core mathematics curriculum accessible to everyone. Toward that end, we have designed the program for use with heterogeneous classes. We provide you with a varied collection of supplemental problems to give you the flexibility to meet individual student needs.

***Teacher Phyllis Quick confers with a group of students.***

## *How is the IMP classroom different?*

When you use the IMP curriculum, your role changes from "imparter of knowledge" to observer and facilitator. You ask challenging questions. You do not give all the answers; rather, you prod students to do their own thinking, to make generalizations, and to go beyond the immediate problem by asking themselves "What if?" The IMP curriculum gives students many opportunities to write about their mathematical thinking, to reflect on what they have done, and to make oral presentations to one another about their work. In IMP, your assessment of students becomes integrated with learning, and you evaluate students according to a variety of criteria, including class participation, daily homework assignments, Problems of the Week, portfolios, and unit assessments. The IMP *Teaching Handbook* provides many practical suggestions on how to get the best possible results using this curriculum in *your* classroom.

## *What is in Year 2 of the IMP curriculum?*

Year 2 of the IMP curriculum contains five units.

### *Solve It!*

The focus of this unit is on using equations to represent real-life situations and on developing the skills to solve these equations. Students begin with situations used in the first year of the curriculum and develop algebraic representations of problems. In order to find solutions to the equations that occur, students explore the concepts of equivalent expressions and equivalent equations. Using these concepts, they develop principles such as the distributive property for working with algebraic expressions and equations, and they learn methods that they can use to solve any linear equation. They also explore the relationship between an algebraic expression, a function, an equation, and a graph, and they examine how to use graphs to solve nonlinear equations.

### *Is There Really a Difference?*

In this unit, students collect data and compare different population groups to one another. In particular, they concentrate on this question:

*If a sample from one population differs in some respect from a sample from a different population, how reliably can you infer that the overall populations differ in that respect?*

They begin by making double bar graphs of some classroom data and explore the process of making and testing hypotheses. Students realize that there is variation even among different samples from the same population, and they see the usefulness of the concept of a *null hypothesis* as they examine this variation. They build on their understanding of standard deviation from the Year 1 unit *The Pit and the Pendulum* and learn that the chi-square ($\chi^2$) statistic can give them the probability of seeing differences of a certain size in samples when the populations are really the same. Their work in this unit culminates in a two-week project in which they propose a hypothesis about two populations that they think really differ in some respect. They then collect sample data about the two populations and analyze their data by using bar graphs, tables, and the $\chi^2$ statistic.

### *Do Bees Build It Best?*

In this unit students work on this problem:

> *Bees store their honey in honeycombs that consist of cells they make out of wax. What is the best design for a honeycomb?*

To analyze this problem, students begin by learning about area and the Pythagorean theorem. Then, using the Pythagorean theorem and trigonometry, students find a formula for the area of a regular polygon with fixed perimeter and find that the larger the number of sides, the larger the area of the polygon. Students then turn their attention to volume and surface area, focusing on prisms that have a regular polygon as the base. They find that for such prisms—if they also want the honeycomb cells to fit together—the mathematical winner, in terms of maximizing volume for a given surface area, is a regular hexagonal prism, which is essentially the choice of the bees.

### *Cookies*

The focus of this unit is on graphing systems of linear inequalities and solving systems of linear equations. Although the central problem is one in linear programming, the major goal of the unit is for students to learn how to manipulate equations and how to reason using graphs.

Students begin by considering a classic type of linear programming problem in which they are asked to maximize the profits of a bakery that makes plain and iced cookies. They are constrained by the amount of ingredients they have on hand and the amount of oven and labor time available. First students work toward a graphical solution of the problem. They see how the linear function can be maximized or minimized by studying the graph. Because the maximum or minimum point they are looking for is often the intersection of two lines, they are motivated to investigate a method for solving two equations in two unknowns. They then return to work in groups on the cookie problem, each group presenting both a solution and a proof that their solution does maximize profits. Finally, each group invents its own linear programming problem and makes a presentation of the problem and its solution to the class.

### *All About Alice*

This unit starts with a model based on Lewis Carroll's *Alice in Wonderland,* a story in which Alice's height is doubled or halved by eating or drinking certain foods she finds. Out of the discussion of this situation come the basic principles for working with exponents—positive, negative, zero, and even fractional—and an introduction to logarithms. Building on the work with exponents, the unit discusses scientific notation and the manipulation of numbers written in scientific notation.

## *How do the four years of the IMP curriculum fit together?*

The four years of the IMP curriculum form an integrated sequence through which students can learn the mathematics they will need both for further education and on the job. Although the organization of the IMP curriculum is very different from the traditional Algebra I-Geometry-Algebra II/Trigonometry-Precalculus sequence, the important mathematical ideas are all there.

Here are some examples of how both traditional concepts and topics new to the high school curriculum are developed:

**Linear equations**

In Year 1 of the IMP curriculum, students develop an intuitive foundation of algebraic thinking, including the use of variables, which they build on throughout the program. In the Year 2 unit *Solve It!,* students use the concept of equivalent equations to see how to solve any linear equation in a single variable. Later in Year 2, in a unit called *Cookies* (about maximizing profits for a bakery), they solve pairs of linear equations in two variables, using both algebraic and geometric methods. In *Meadows or Malls?* (Year 3), they extend those ideas to systems with more than two variables, and see how to use matrices and the technology of graphing calculators to solve such systems.

**Measurement and the Pythagorean theorem**

Measurement, including area and volume, is one of the fundamental topics in geometry. The Pythagorean theorem is one of the most important geometric principles ever discovered. In the Year 2 unit *Do Bees Build It Best?,* students combine these ideas with their knowledge of similarity (from the Year 1 unit *Shadows*) to see why the hexagonal prism of the bees' honeycomb design is the most efficient regular prism possible. Students also use the Pythagorean theorem in later units, applying it to develop such principles as the distance formula in coordinate geometry.

**Trigonometric functions**

In traditional programs, the trigonometric functions are introduced in the eleventh or twelfth grade. In the IMP curriculum, students begin working with trigonometry in Year 1 (in *Shadows*), using right-triangle trigonometry in several units in Years 2 and 3 (including *Do Bees Build It Best?*). In the Year 4 unit *High Dive,* they extend trigonometry from right triangles to circular functions, in the context of a circus act in which a performer falls from a Ferris wheel into a moving tub of water. (In *High Dive,* students also learn principles of physics, developing laws for falling objects and using vectors to find vertical and horizontal components of velocity.)

**Standard deviation and the binomial distribution**

Standard deviation and the binomial distribution are major tools in the study of probability and statistics. *The Game of Pig* gets students started by building a firm understanding of concepts of probability and the phenomenon of experimental variation. Later in Year 1 (in *The Pit and the Pendulum*), they use standard deviation to see that the period of a pendulum is determined primarily by its length. In Year 2, they compare standard deviation with the chi-square test in examining whether the difference between two sets of data is statistically significant. In *Pennant Fever* (Year 3), students use the binomial distribution to evaluate a team's chances of winning the baseball championship, and in *The Pollster's Dilemma* (Year 4), students tie many of these ideas together in the central limit theorem, seeing how the margin of error and the level of certainty for an election poll depend on its size.

## *Does the program work?*

The IMP curriculum has been thoroughly field-tested and enthusiastically received by hundreds of classroom teachers around the country. Their enthusiasm is based on the success they have seen in their own classrooms with their own students. For instance, IMP teacher Dennis Cavaillé says, "For the first time in my teaching career, I see lots of students excited about solving math problems inside *and* outside of class."

These informal observations are backed up by more formal evaluations. Dr. Norman Webb of the Wisconsin Center for Education Research has done several studies comparing the performance of students using the IMP curriculum with the performance of students in traditional programs. For instance, he has found that IMP students do as well as students in traditional mathematics classes on standardized tests such as the SAT. This is especially significant because IMP students spend about twenty-five percent of their time studying topics, such as statistics, not covered on these tests. To measure IMP students' achievement in these other areas, Dr. Webb conducted three separate studies involving students at different grade levels and in different locations. The three tests used in these studies involved statistics, quantitative reasoning, and general problem solving. In all three cases, the IMP students outperformed their counterparts in traditional programs by a statistically significant margin, even though the two groups began with equivalent scores on eighth grade standardized tests.

But one of our proudest achievements is that IMP students are excited about mathematics, as shown by Dr. Webb's finding that they take more mathematics courses in high school than their counterparts in traditional programs. We think this is because they see that mathematics can be relevant to their own lives. If so, then the program works.

Dan Fendel

Diane Resek

Lynne Alper

Sherry Fraser

# Note to Students

This textbook represents the second year of a four-year program of mathematics learning and investigation. As in the first year, the program is organized around interesting, complex problems, and the concepts you learn grow out of what you'll need to solve those problems.

***These pages in the student book welcome students to the program.***

## • *If you studied IMP Year 1*

If you studied IMP Year 1, then you know the excitement of problem-based mathematical study, such as devising strategies for a complex dice game, learning the history of the Overland Trail, and experimenting with pendulums.

The Year 2 program extends and expands the challenges that you worked with in Year 1. For instance:

- In Year 1, you began developing a foundation for working with variables. In Year 2, you will build on this foundation in units that demonstrate the power of algebra to solve problems, including some that look back at situations from Year 1 units.
- In Year 1, you used principles of statistics to help predict the period of a 30-foot pendulum. In Year 2, you will learn another statistical method, one that will help you to understand statistical comparisons of populations. One important part of your work will be to prepare, conduct, and analyze your own survey.

You'll also use ideas from geometry to understand why the design of bees' honeycombs is so efficient, and you'll use graphs to help a bakery decide how many plain and iced cookies they should make to maximize their profits. Year 2 closes with a literary adventure—you'll use Lewis Carroll's classic *Alice's Adventures in Wonderland* to explore and extend the meaning of exponents.

- *If you didn't study IMP Year 1*

If this is your first experience with the Interactive Mathematics Program (IMP), you can rely on your classmates and your teacher to fill in what you've missed. Meanwhile, here are some things you should know about the program, how it was developed, and how it is organized.

The Interactive Mathematics Program is the product of a collaboration of teachers, teacher-educators, and mathematicians who have been working together since 1989 to reform the way high school mathematics is taught. About one hundred thousand students and five hundred teachers used these materials before they were published. Their experiences, reactions, and ideas have been incorporated into this final version.

Our goal is to give you the mathematics you need in order to succeed in this changing world. We want to present mathematics to you in a manner that reflects how mathematics is used and that reflects the different ways people work and learn together. Through this perspective on mathematics, you will be prepared both for continued study of mathematics in college and for the world of work.

This book contains the various assignments that will be your work during Year 2 of the program. As you will see, these problems require ideas from many branches of mathematics, including algebra, geometry, probability, graphing, statistics, and trigonometry. Rather than present each of these areas separately, we have integrated them and presented them in meaningful contexts, so you will see how they relate to each other and to our world.

Each unit in this four-year program has a central problem or theme, and focuses on several major mathematical ideas. Within each unit, the material is organized for teaching purposes into "days," with a homework assignment for each day. (Your class may not follow this schedule exactly, especially if it doesn't meet every day.)

At the end of the main material for each unit, you will find a set of supplementary problems. These problems provide you with additional opportunities to work with ideas from the unit, either to strengthen your understanding of the core material or to explore new ideas related to the unit.

Although the IMP program is not organized into courses called "Algebra," "Geometry," and so on, you will be learning all the essential mathematical concepts that are part of those traditional courses. You will also be learning concepts from branches of mathematics—especially statistics and probability—that are not part of a traditional high school program.

To accomplish your goals, you will have to be an active learner, because the book does not teach directly. Your role as a mathematics student will be to experiment, to investigate, to ask questions, to make and test conjectures, and to reflect, and then to communicate your ideas and conclusions both orally and in writing. You will do some of your work in collaboration with fellow students, just as users of mathematics in the real world often work in teams. At other times, you will be working on your own.

We hope you will enjoy the challenge of this new way of learning mathematics and will see mathematics in a new light.

Dan Fendel Diane Resek Lynne Alper Sherry Fraser

# Finding What You Need

We designed this guide to help you find what you need amid all the information it provides. Each of the following components has a special treatment in the layout of the guide.

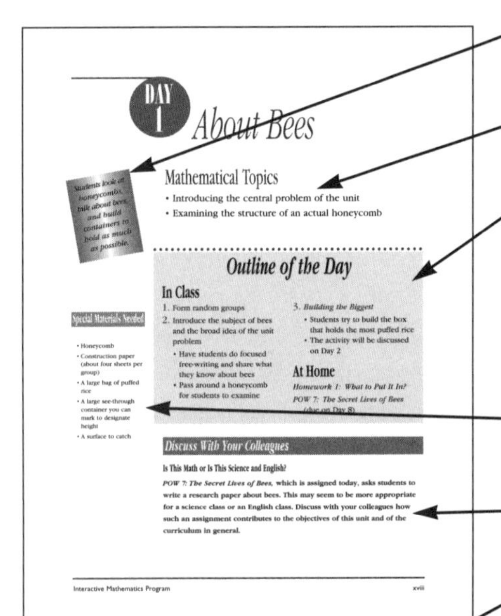

DAY 1

About Bees

Students look at honeycombs, talk about bees, and build containers to hold as much as possible.

Mathematical Topics

- Introducing the central problem of the unit
- Examining the structure of an actual honeycomb

Outline of the Day

In Class

1. Form random groups
2. Introduce the subject of bees and the broad idea of the unit problem
   - Have students do focused free-writing and share what they know about bees
   - Pass around a honeycomb for students to examine
3. *Building the Biggest*
   - Students try to build the box that holds the most puffed rice
   - The activity will be discussed on Day 2

At Home

*Homework 1: What to Put It In?*

*POW 7: The Secret Lives of Bees* (due on Day 8)

Special Materials Needed

- Honeycomb
- Construction paper (about four sheets per group)
- A large bag of puffed rice
- A large see-through container you can mark to designate height
- A surface to catch

Discuss With Your Colleagues

Is This Math or Is This Science and English?

***POW 7: The Secret Lives of Bees*, which is assigned today, asks students to write a research paper about bees. This may seem to be more appropriate for a science class or an English class. Discuss with your colleagues how such an assignment contributes to the objectives of this unit and of the curriculum in general.**

Interactive Mathematics Program xviii

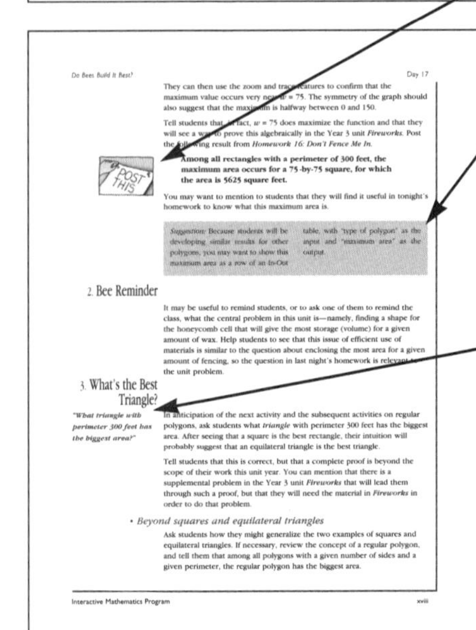

Do Bees Build It Best? Day 17

They can then use the zoom and trace features to confirm that the maximum value occurs very near $w = 75$. The symmetry of the graph should also suggest that the maximum is halfway between 0 and 150.

Tell students that, in fact, $w = 75$ does maximize the function and that they will see a way to prove this algebraically in the Year 3 unit *Fireworks*. Post the following result from *Homework 16: Don't Fence Me In*.

**Among all rectangles with a perimeter of 300 feet, the maximum area occurs for a 75-by-75 square, for which the area is 5625 square feet.**

You may want to mention to students that they will find it useful in tonight's homework to know what this maximum area is.

*Suggestion:* Because students will be developing similar results for other polygons, you may want to show this maximum area as a row of an In-Out table, with "type of polygon" as the input and "maximum area" as the output.

2. Bee Reminder

It may be useful to remind students, or to ask one of them to remind the class, what the central problem in this unit is—namely, finding a shape for the honeycomb cell that will give the most storage (volume) for a given amount of wax. Help students to see that this issue of efficient use of materials is similar to the question about enclosing the most area for a given amount of fencing, so the question in last night's homework is relevant to the unit problem.

3. What's the Best Triangle?

***"What triangle with perimeter 300 feet has the biggest area?"***

In anticipation of the next activity and the subsequent activities on regular polygons, ask students what *triangle* with perimeter 300 feet has the biggest area. After seeing that a square is the best rectangle, their intuition will probably suggest that an equilateral triangle is the best triangle.

Tell students that this is correct, but that a complete proof is beyond the scope of their work this unit year. You can mention that there is a supplemental problem in the Year 3 unit *Fireworks* that will lead them through such a proof, but that they will need the material in *Fireworks* in order to do that problem.

- *Beyond squares and equilateral triangles*

Ask students how they might generalize the two examples of squares and equilateral triangles. If necessary, review the concept of a regular polygon, and tell them that among all polygons with a given number of sides and a given perimeter, the regular polygon has the biggest area.

Interactive Mathematics Program xviii

**Synopsis of the Day:** The key idea or activity for each day is summarized in a brief sentence or two.

**Mathematical Topics:** Mathematical issues for the day are presented in a bulleted list.

**Outline of the Day:** Under the *In Class* heading, the outline summarizes the activities for the day, which are keyed to numbered headings in the discussion. Daily homework assignments and Problems of the Week are listed under the *At Home* heading.

**Special Materials Needed:** Special items needed in the classroom for each day are bulleted here.

**Discuss With Your Colleagues:** This section highlights topics that you may want to discuss with your peers.

**Post This:** The *Post This* icon indicates items that you may want to display in the classroom.

**Asides:** These are ideas outside the main thrust of a discussion. They include background information, refinements, or subtle points that may only be of interest to some students, ways to help fill in gaps in understanding the main ideas, and suggestions about when to bring in a particular concept.

**Suggested Questions:** These are specific questions that you might ask during an activity or discussion to promote student insight or to determine whether students understand an idea. The appropriateness of these questions generally depends on what students have already developed or presented on their own.

## Icons for Student Written Products

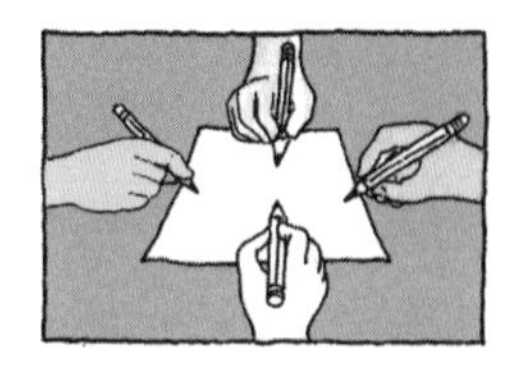

***Single Group report***

***Individual reports***

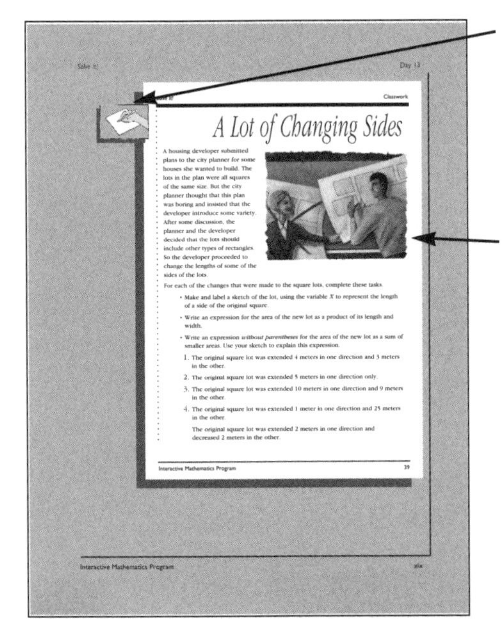

Day 13

Classwork

A Lot of Changing Sides

A housing developer submitted plans to the city planner for some houses she wanted to build. The lots in the plan were all squares of the same size. But the city planner thought that this plan was boring and insisted that the developer introduce some variety. After some discussion, the planner and the developer decided that the lots should include other types of rectangles. So the developer proceeded to change the lengths of some of the sides of the lots.

For each of the changes that were made to the square lots, complete these tasks.

- Make and label a sketch of the lot, using the variable $X$ to represent the length of a side of the original square.
- Write an expression for the area of the new lot as a product of its length and width.
- Write an expression *without parentheses* for the area of the new lot as a sum of smaller areas. Use your sketch to explain this expression.

1. The original square lot was extended 4 meters in one direction and 3 meters in the other.
2. The original square lot was extended 5 meters in one direction only.
3. The original square lot was extended 10 meters in one direction and 9 meters in the other.
4. The original square lot was extended 1 meter in one direction and 25 meters in the other.

The original square lot was extended 2 meters in one direction and decreased 2 meters in the other.

Interactive Mathematics Program 39

Interactive Mathematics Program xix

**Icons for Student Written Products:** For each group activity, there is an icon suggesting a single group report, individual reports, or no report at all. If graphs are included, the icon indicates this as well. (The graph icons do not appear in every unit.)

**Embedded Student Pages:** The teacher guide contains reduced-size copies of the pages from the student book, including the "transition pages" that appear occasionally within each unit to summarize each portion of the unit and to prepare students for what is coming. The reduced-size classwork and homework assignments follow the teacher notes for the day on which the activity is begun. Having all of these student pages in the teacher's guide is a helpful way for you to see things from the students' perspective.

# Additional Information

Here is a brief outline of other tools we have included to assist you and make both the teaching and the learning experience more rewarding.

**Glossary:** This section, which is found at the back of the book, gives the definitions of important terms for all of Year 2 for easy reference. The same glossary appears in the student book.

**Appendix A: Supplemental Problems:** This appendix contains a variety of interesting additional activities for the unit, for teachers who would like to supplement material found in the regular classroom problems. These additional activities are of two types—*reinforcements,* which help increase student understanding of concepts that are central to the unit, and *extensions,* which allow students to explore ideas beyond the basic unit.

**Appendix B: Blackline Masters:** For each unit, this appendix contains materials you can reproduce that are not available in the student book and that will be helpful to teacher and student alike. They include the end-of-unit assessments as well as such items as diagrams from which you can make transparencies. Semester assessments for Year 2 are included in *Do Bees Build It Best?* (for first semester) and *All About Alice* (for second semester).

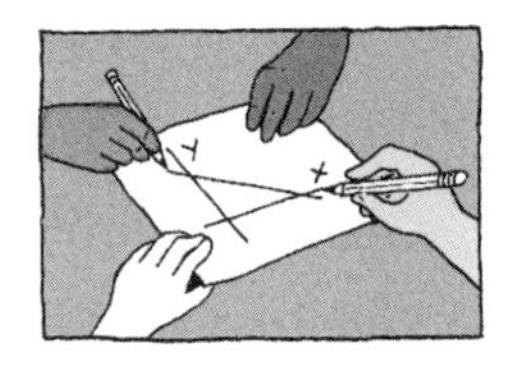

***Single group graph***

***Individual graphs***

***No report at all***

# Year 2 IMP Units

***Solve It!***

***Is There Really a Difference?***

***Do Bees Build It Best?***

***Cookies***

***All About Alice*** **(in this book)**

Contents

# "All About Alice" Overview

## Summary of the Unit

*"Curiouser and curiouser!" cried Alice. "Now I'm opening out like the largest telescope that ever was! Goodbye, feet!"*

In Lewis Carroll's *Alice's Adventures in Wonderland,* Alice finds a magical cake that makes her grow larger and a magical beverage that makes her grow smaller. This unit uses Alice's predicament, made more specific, as the motivation for extending the operation of exponentiation from positive integer exponents to zero, negative, and fractional exponents.

Students see that the standard definition of exponentiation in terms of repeated multiplication breaks down. They then use a variety of approaches to see what makes sense for the broader definition.

- They use the Alice metaphor: eating an ounce of cake doubles Alice's height and drinking an ounce of beverage halves her height. The fact that the cake and the beverage "cancel out" suggests an interpretation for negative exponents, and the idea of breaking up whole ounces into fractional pieces helps give meaning to fractions as exponents.
- They develop the basic laws of exponents, such as $a^b \cdot a^c = a^{b+c}$ and $(a^b)^c = a^{bc}$, based on positive integer exponents, and see what definitions for negative and fractional exponents are consistent with these laws.
- They look at the graphs of functions like $y = 2^x$ for positive integer values of $x$ and see how these can be made into smooth curves for other values of $x$.
- They look at the numerical patterns for expressions with positive integer exponents and extend those patterns.

The study of exponents provides a natural context for an introduction to logarithms. There are two main approaches used for this idea.

- Abstractly, logarithms answer questions of the form "What value of $x$ solves the equation $a^x = b$?"
- In terms of the Alice metaphor, logarithms tell us "How much cake is needed?" in order to multiply Alice's height by a given factor.

Students learn to connect these two approaches, and they go back and forth between them.

Finally, the work with exponents serves as the basis for the introduction of scientific notation and order of magnitude. Students see how to do arithmetic using scientific notation and connect the notation with the Alice metaphor.

This outline gives a summary of the unit's overall organization.

- Days 1-2: Introduction to the metaphor of the cake and the beverage
- Days 3-5: Zero as an exponent and the additive law of exponents
- Days 6-8: Negative exponents
- Days 9-11: Fractional exponents
- Days 12-13: Summarizing ideas about exponents
- Days 14-15: Logarithms
- Days 16-17: Scientific notation
- Day 18-20: Portfolios, assessments, and summing up

## *Concepts and Skills*

The operation of exponentiation is the primary focus of this unit, as students extend the operation and study related ideas such as logarithms and scientific notation. The process of extending exponentiation is explored through several approaches—a contextual situation, algebraic laws, graphing, and number patterns—as outlined in the unit summary above.

Here are the main concepts and skills that students encounter and practice during the course of this unit, summarized by category.

### *Extending the operation of exponentiation*

- Defining the operation for an exponent of zero
- Defining the operation for negative integer exponents
- Defining the operation for fractional exponents

### *Laws of exponents*

- Developing the additive law of exponents
- Developing the law of repeated exponentiation

### *Graphing*

- Describing the graphs of exponential functions
- Comparing graphs of exponential functions for different bases

- Describing the graphs of logarithmic functions
- Comparing graphs of logarithmic functions for different bases

*Logarithms*

- Understanding the meaning of logarithms
- Making connections between exponential and logarithmic equations

*Scientific notation*

- Converting numbers from ordinary notation to scientific notation, and vice versa
- Developing principles for computation using scientific notation
- Using the concept of *order of magnitude* in estimation

In addition to the concepts and skills described here, students will work with concepts of logical reasoning in connection with the two POWs in the unit.

## Materials

In addition to providing standard materials, such as graphing calculators, transparencies, chart paper, marking pens, you may want to use the video *Powers of Ten* to summarize the unit. (*Powers of Ten* is available from Pyramid Films, PO Box 1048, Santa Monica, CA 90406.) If you use the video, you will need a video player as well. You may also want to make a transparency of the graph in Appendix B.

Students need to provide these materials:

- Scientific calculator (for use at home)
- Graph paper

## Grading

The IMP *Teaching Handbook* contains general guidelines about how to grade students in an IMP class. You will probably want to check daily that students have done their homework and include the regular completion of homework as part of students' grades. Your grading scheme will probably also include Problems of the Week, the unit portfolio, and the end-of-unit assessments.

Because you will not be able to read thoroughly every assignment that students turn in, you will need to select certain assignments to read carefully and to base grades on. Here are some suggestions.

- *Homework 1: Graphing Alice*
- *Having Your Cake and Drinking Too* (Day 6)

- *Homework 8: Negative Reflections*
- *All Roads Lead to Rome* (Day 12)
- *Homework 14: Alice on a Log*

If you want to base your grading on more tasks, there are many other homework assignments, class activities, and oral presentations you can use.

# Interactive Mathematics Program

IMP™

Integrated High School Mathematics

## All About Alice

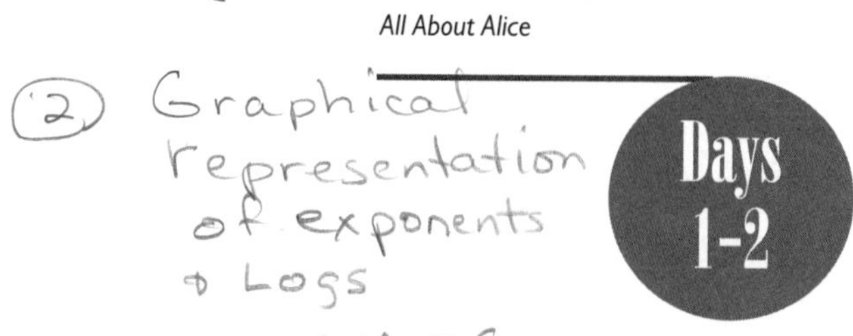


# Who's Alice?

***This page in the student book introduces Days 1 and 2.***

Once upon a time, a man wrote a story about the adventures of an imaginary girl named Alice, who traveled to a place called Wonderland. This story became the best-selling children's book of all time in England. The author used the pen name Lewis Carroll, and he wrote books about mathematical logic in addition to his fiction about Alice. In this unit, one of Alice's adventures forms the basis for you to explore some ideas about numerical operations, graphs, and algebraic formulas.

***Discussing homework, Mara Campbell, Nick Cabrul, and Amy McDonald compare the graphs they made of Alice's height changes.***

*Students learn about Alice and the strange cake and beverage she finds.*

## Mathematical Topics

- Introducing a metaphor for thinking about exponents

## *Outline of the Day*

### In Class

1. Form random groups
2. *Alice in Wonderland*
   - Introduce the story of Alice
   - Students examine what happens if Alice eats or drinks various quantities of cake or beverage
   - The activity will be discussed on Day 2
3. Introduce *POW 14: More from Lewis Carroll*

### At Home

Homework 1: Graphing Alice

*POW 17: More from Lewis Carroll* (due Day 9)

## *Discuss With Your Colleagues*

### The Role of the Syllogism

**In traditional high school geometry courses, students often devote considerable time to the study of formal reasoning, including the role of the syllogism. (This is a name for the type of reasoning that leads from the statements "Socrates is a man" and "All men are mortal" to the conclusion "Socrates is mortal.") *POW 14: More from Lewis Carroll* asks students to use this type of reasoning, though in a less formal setting.**

**What role should formal logic play in the high school curriculum? What was your own experience with this type of reasoning?**

## 1. Forming Groups

At the beginning of the unit, place students in new groups as described in the IMP *Teaching Handbook*. We recommend that you create new groups again on Day 11.

*Note:* Students will need scientific calculators at home for many assignments in this unit.

## 2. *Alice in Wonderland*

This unit is a bit different from most other units in that there is no central unit problem to solve. Instead, there is a general context to the unit, the study of what happens to Alice in different situations in Wonderland. (The unit is somewhat like the Year 1 unit *The Overland Trail* in this respect.)

Wait until at least Day 2 before discussing which mathematical topics will be studied in this unit, because doing so now may undermine the discovery that Alice's height is related to exponents. Also, students may feel that they already "know exponents" and therefore may not invest themselves completely in the Alice model.

The activity *Alice in Wonderland* introduces the major metaphor of the unit and gets students thinking about how exponents work. The metaphor plays an important role in the development of the unit. It will be used to motivate students and to help them extend the definition of exponentiation beyond whole-number exponents and understand laws relating to exponents.

It is important that students have a positive feeling about this metaphor. You can begin creating this feeling by introducing the broad outline of Lewis Carroll's story *Alice's Adventures in Wonderland* or by asking a student to do so. Many of your students may not be familiar with the story.

To refresh your memory, the story begins with a young girl, named Alice, seeing a white rabbit who is carrying a pocket watch and mutters about how late he is. Alice follows him down a rabbit hole to a tea party with the Mad Hatter and then goes on to have many other adventures.

Have the class read the excerpt from the story provided here and the paragraphs that immediately follow the excerpt (but not the questions).

### • *Acting out "doubling"*

It's helpful to have students "act out" the idea of Alice's growth in some way before they try to answer the questions in the activity. The goal of this demonstration is to give them a concrete sense of the impact of repeated doubling.

For example, you can give each group (or pair of students) a long strip of cash register paper, perhaps about 20 feet. Then have them repeatedly fold it in half so that they see how quickly halving makes it get smaller.

Here are two ways to act out the doubling process.

- Go to the school auditorium and have the class stand in front of the first row. Then send one student to the aisle at the first row, another to the second row, another to the fourth row, another to the eighth row, and so on. To dramatize the process, you might have the rest of the students close their eyes before each additional student moves to the new position.
- Use the bleachers of the school stadium to enact a similar process. Again, this will be most dramatic if the rest of the students close their eyes while the selected students go to their positions.

### • *The questions*

With this introduction, have students work on the activity's questions in groups. The activity will be discussed tomorrow. (You should leave some time today to introduce the new POW.)

Nowhere in the problem are we told how tall Alice is; we only know by how much her height is multiplied. Some students may not like working with this kind of abstraction. You can suggest that they make the situation more concrete by picking a particular height for Alice as a starting point. But they should focus on the comparison between her starting height and her final height, asking, "By how much has her height been multiplied?"

## 3. Introduction to *POW 14: More from Lewis Carroll*

POW 14, scheduled for discussion on Day 9, is based on some Lewis Carroll problems about logic and deduction. This POW is much more directed than usual, but the subject matter is likely to be foreign to many students. The problem does have an open-ended "make-up-your-own" component.

You should take some time to introduce this POW and to discuss the examples. Point out that we are not claiming that any of the individual statements are actually true. Instead, we are focusing on what conclusions we could draw *if* they were true. You might also point out that students don't even necessarily have to understand what the words in the statements all mean. For example, they don't need to know that a geranium is a flower.

## *Homework 1: Graphing Alice*

This homework is a contination of the classwork from today.

# Alice in Wonderland

In 1865, a book was published that was to become the most popular children's book in England—*Alice's Adventures in Wonderland*. The author used the pen name Lewis Carroll, but his real name was Charles L. Dodgson (1832–1898). He also wrote *Through the Looking Glass, and What Alice Found There,* a sequel to his original Alice story.

*Continued on next page*

# The Situation of Alice

Here is an excerpt from *Alice's Adventures in Wonderland.* Read the excerpt, and then answer the questions below.

> [Alice] found a little bottle . . . , and tied round the neck of the bottle was a paper label with the words "DRINK ME" beautifully printed in large letters. . . .
>
> So Alice ventured to taste it, and, finding it very nice . . . , she very soon finished it off.
>
> "What a curious feeling!" said Alice. "I must be shutting up like a telescope!"
>
> And so it was indeed: she was now only ten inches high. . . .
>
> Soon her eye fell on a little glass box that was lying under the table: she opened it, and found in it a very small cake, on which the words "EAT ME" were beautifully marked in currants. . . .
>
> She ate a little bit . . . and very soon finished off the cake.
>
> "Curiouser and curiouser!" cried Alice. . . . "Now I'm opening out like the largest telescope that ever was! Goodbye, feet!" (for when she looked down at her feet, they seemed to be almost out of sight, they were getting so far off). . . .
>
> Just at this moment her head struck against the roof of the hall.

# The Questions

In Lewis Carroll's story, whenever Alice drinks the beverage from the bottle, she gets smaller, and when she eats the cake, she gets bigger. But Carroll doesn't say *how much bigger* or *how much smaller,* or even *how tall Alice was to start with.*

Assume that for every ounce of the cake Alice eats, her height doubles, and for every ounce of the beverage she drinks, her height is cut in half. Answer these questions based on that assumption.

1. What happens to Alice's height if she eats 2 ounces of cake? What if she eats 5 ounces?
2. Find a rule for what happens to Alice's height when she eats $C$ ounces of cake. Explain your rule.
3. What happens to Alice's height if she drinks 4 ounces of beverage? What if she drinks 6 ounces?
4. Find a rule for what happens to Alice's height when she drinks $B$ ounces of beverage. Explain your rule.

Math Goal: deductive reasoning
If then statements



structured thinking
deductive thinking
way mathematics was done
this way



# POW 14 *More from Lewis Carroll*

Lewis Carroll was a mathematician as well as a novelist. One of his special mathematical interests was **logic,** which might be described as the mathematical science of formal reasoning. Logic analyzes how to draw legitimate, or *valid,* conclusions from true statements. This process of drawing conclusions is also called **deduction.**

In one of Lewis Carroll's books, he gave problems involving groups of statements. The reader was supposed to figure out what, if anything, could be deduced from the statements, that is, what new conclusions could be drawn. All of the groups of statements in this POW are taken directly from Lewis Carroll's work.

Here are two examples.

## *Example 1*

a. John is in the house.

b. Everyone in the house is ill.

If you know that statements a and b are both true, then you can deduce that John must be ill. So "John is ill" is a valid conclusion.

*Continued on next page*

## Example 2

a. Some geraniums are red.

b. All these flowers are red.

In this case, knowing that statements a and b are both true does not tell you whether any or all of "these flowers" are geraniums. They might be other kinds of red flowers. So there isn't anything new that you can definitely deduce from the two statements in Example 2.

## Part I: Finding Conclusions

Examine each of the sets of statements given here. Decide what, *if anything,* you could deduce if you knew that the given statements were true. (There may be more than one conclusion possible. Give as many conclusions as you can.)

Explain in each case why you think your conclusions are correct or why you think no new conclusions can be deduced. Diagrams or pictures might be helpful both in analyzing the statements and in explaining your reasoning.

1. a. No medicine is nice.

   b. Senna is a medicine.

2. a. All shillings are round.

   b. These coins are round.

3. a. Some pigs are wild.

   b. All pigs are fat.

4. a. Prejudiced persons are untrustworthy.

   b. Some unprejudiced persons are disliked.

5. a. Babies are illogical.

   b. Nobody who is despised can manage a crocodile.

   c. Illogical persons are despised.

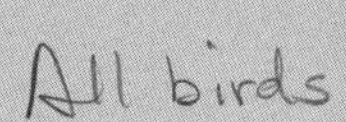


6. a. No birds, except ostriches, are 9 feet high.

   b. There are no birds in this aviary that belong to anyone but me.

   c. No ostrich lives on mince pies.

   d. I have no birds less than 9 feet high.

*Continued on next page*

## Part II: Creating Examples

Make up two sets of statements similar to those in Part I. One of your sets should have a valid conclusion, and the other should not.

## Write-up

1. *Process*
2. *Results:* Give your conclusions (with explanations) for each set of statements in Part I. Give your sets of statements for Part II and explain why they do or do not have valid conclusions.
3. *Evaluation:* What does this POW have to do with mathematics?
4. *Self-assessment*

Examples 1 and 2 and the statements in Part I are taken from *Symbolic Logic and The Game of Logic,* by Lewis Carroll, Dover Publications, Inc., New York and Berkeley Enterprises, 1958.

# Homework 1 — Graphing Alice

In the activity *Alice in Wonderland*, you looked at what happened to Alice's height in various situations. This assignment involves looking at that information in an organized way.

Choose a suitable scale for each of the graphs you create. (*Note:* The scales of the two axes do not need to be the same.)

1. Alice's height changes when she eats the cake. Assume as before that her height doubles for each ounce she eats.

   a. Find out what Alice's height is multiplied by when she eats 1, 2, 3, 4, 5, or 6 ounces of cake.

   b. Make a graph of this information.

2. Alice's height also changes when she drinks the beverage. Assume as before that her height is halved for each ounce she drinks.

   a. Find out what Alice's height is multiplied by when she drinks 1, 2, 3, 4, 5, or 6 ounces of beverage.

   b. Make a graph of this information.

3. Suppose Alice found a different kind of cake, one that tripled her height for every ounce consumed. Do Questions 1a and 1b for this different cake.

4. Suppose Alice found a different kind of beverage, one that cut her height to one-third of its measure for every ounce consumed. Do Questions 2a and 2b for this different beverage.

5. Compare and contrast the graphs from Questions 1 through 4. In general, what do you think is true of graphs such as these?

# What Happened to Alice?

*Students develop some general formulas for what happens to Alice.*

## Mathematical Topics

- Using powers of 2 to generalize the Alice metaphor
- Working with exponents on the graphing calculator and on scientific calculators
- Graphing exponential functions with different bases

## Outline of the Day

### In Class

1. Discuss *Alice in Wonderland* (from Day 1)
   - Develop the general expression $2^C$ for Alice's growth factor when she eats $C$ ounces of cake
   - Develop the general expression $\frac{1}{2^B}$ for Alice's growth factor when she drinks $B$ ounces of beverage
   - Introduce terms such as *base 2 cake* and *base 2 beverage*
   - Discuss informally what happens in the graphs as $x$ moves to the left
2. Discuss *Homework 1: Graphing Alice*
   - Post the graph from Question 1 (students will add to this during the unit)

### At Home

*Homework 2: A Wonderland Lost*

### Special Materials Needed

- Graph paper transparency

*Note:* We recommend that you begin today with the discussion of yesterday's activity, *Alice in Wonderland,* and use that as the basis for the discussion of last night's homework.

# 1. Discussion of *Alice in Wonderland*

You can begin by having a club card student present Questions 1 and 2, and let the rest of the class comment and elaborate. Then have another club card student present Questions 3 and 4, and solicit reactions and comments on that.

You can use material in the subsections "Eating $C$ ounces of cake" and "Drinking $B$ ounces of beverage" for guidance on what needs to come out of these presentations. If a particular idea does not come across clearly from the presentation, you should pursue it through questions to the class, as suggested in those subsections.

## • *Eating C ounces of cake*

Students should see that if Alice eats one ounce, then one more ounce, and so on, her height will be doubled each time so that overall, if she eats $C$ ounces, her height will be multiplied by $2^C$. It is important that this fundamental generalization be very clear.

***"Is there another way to write 2 • 2? What if C 2's were multiplied together?"***

***"What do we call the number 2 in the expression $2^C$? What do we call C?"***

If necessary, have the presenter explain the specific cases in Question 1. You can ask questions to bring out the use of an exponential expression in Question 2.

Ask the class for the terms used to describe the numbers 2 and $C$ in an expression such as $2^C$. If no one remembers, remind students of the words *base* and *exponent*.

When we say that eating $C$ ounces of cake multiplies Alice's height by $2^C$, we are implicitly assuming that eating $C$ ounces of cake is the same as eating those $C$ ounces one ounce at a time. This issue is important in the discussion of the activity *Piece After Piece* (on Day 4).

The generalization that eating $C$ ounces of cake multiplies Alice's height by $2^C$ also involves the fact that if something is multiplied first by one factor (say, $a$) and then the resulting product is multiplied by another factor (say, $b$), then the original number has been multiplied altogether by $ab$. Thus, if the first ounce of cake doubles Alice's height, and the second doubles her height again, then altogether her height has been multiplied by $2 \cdot 2$, or 4. This is essentially the associative property of multiplication, because it states that $(h \cdot 2) \cdot 2 = h \cdot (2 \cdot 2)$, where $h$ represents Alice's original height.

## • *Drinking B ounces of beverage*

The beverage aspect of the situation typically is somewhat more difficult for students than the cake aspect of the situation. Students need to see that drinking $B$ ounces of the beverage multiplies Alice's height by $\frac{1}{2^B}$. *Note:* It's fine if they write this instead as $(\frac{1}{2})^B$.

Actually, students probably are more likely to see the change in Alice's height in terms of division (dividing by $2^B$) than in terms of multiplication. But the unit will proceed more smoothly if they focus on the question, "What is Alice's height multiplied by?"

***"What is another way to express division by 2?" or "How can you express this in terms of multiplication?"***

If students use division initially, you can ask some leading questions to help them make this transition, phrasing your questions in fairly explicit terms if necessary.

***If students say an ounce of beverage multiplies Alice's height by 0.5, ask: "How else can you write 0.5?"***

It is also important that students express this multiplication factor as a fraction rather than as a decimal. Doing so will help make the pattern clear and will help extend the operation of exponentiation to include negative exponents. Again, some leading questions from you may be helpful.

The fact that drinking $B$ ounces of beverage multiplies Alice's height by $\frac{1}{2^B}$ can be seen by students as the consequence of two basic ideas.

- Multiplying Alice's height by $\frac{1}{2}$ repeatedly, $B$ times, is the same as multiplying by $(\frac{1}{2})^B$.
- Multiplying by $(\frac{1}{2})^B$ is the same as multiplying by $\frac{1}{2^B}$. In other words,

$$\left(\frac{1}{2}\right)^B = \frac{1^B}{2^B} = \frac{1}{2^B}$$

Students may not reason this way, however. You can introduce these ideas gradually, asking students what Alice's height is multiplied by when she drinks specific amounts and then asking them to restate the result.

For example, if they see that drinking 3 ounces means that Alice's height is multiplied by $\frac{1}{8}$, you can ask where the number 8 comes from. (It will be easier to pose this type of question if students write the multiplying factor as the fraction $\frac{1}{8}$, not the decimal 0.125.) However, even after examples like this, many students will continue to see drinking multiple ounces of beverage as repeatedly dividing Alice's height by 2, rather than repeatedly multiplying it by $\frac{1}{2}$.

## • *Exponents on calculators*

If students have never worked with exponents on their graphing calculators, they should figure out how to do so now. They should also learn how to do this operation on their own scientific calculators. Most such calculators have a "$y^x$" key that is used for computing the values of exponential expressions. For example, to find $5^7$, simply press this key sequence:

| 5 | $y^x$ | 7 |
|---|---|---|

## 2. Discussion of *Homework 1: Graphing Alice*

Now turn to a discussion of last night's homework. As students discuss Questions 1 through 4, you can have them make chart paper versions of their work, so that all four graphs can be compared easily when the class gets to Question 5.

*Note:* Students are expected only to plot individual points for the graphs in Questions 1 through 4, using specific positive integer values for $x$; they are not asked to plot the complete functions. As the unit progresses, they will gradually move toward the complete graphs of functions such as $y = 2^x$.

### • *Question 1*

***If needed:***
***"Is the difference between $2^2$ and $2^3$ the same as the difference between $2^3$ and $2^4$?"***

Probably, the main focus for the discussion of Question 1 will be on the scaling of the axes. One error that many students make is to scale the $y$-axis so that the values $2^1$, $2^2$, $2^3$, $2^4$, and so on, are equally spaced. If students do this, they will get linear graphs. If the presenter for Question 1 makes this mistake, you can ask a general question about scaling to bring this out.

When the graph is scaled correctly, students should see that Alice's height does not grow in a linear fashion. That is, the points on the graph for Question 1 do not lie on a straight line.

***"Using f to represent the function, how do you write an equation for this graph using***

Ask students to express the rule for the graph using function notation. For example, if they use the letter $f$ for the function and $x$ for the independent variable, they will probably write $f(x) = 2^x$.

Once the graph is done, you should post it on chart paper, labeling it appropriately, so that students can refer to it and add to it as the definition of exponentiation is extended during the unit.

You may need to emphasize that the scale for the $x$-axis and the scale for the $y$-axis do not need to be the same. In fact, for this problem, if the scales are not different, the graph will be very high in comparison to its width.

- *Question 2*

The issues that arise for Question 2 likely will be similar to those for Question 1. Students should see that they need to use a different scale for the $y$-axis for Question 2 than was used for Question 1.

Have students express this function in function notation, using a different letter from that used in Question 1. For instance, students might write this as $g(x) = \left(\frac{1}{2}\right)^x$.

- *Questions 3 and 4*

In discussing Questions 3 and 4, elicit generalizations analogous to those developed in the discussion of *Alice in Wonderland*. That is, students should see that if Alice eats $C$ ounces of the cake from Question 3, her height is multiplied by $3^C$, and if she drinks $B$ ounces of the beverage from Question 4, her height is multiplied by $\frac{1}{3^B}$.

Introduce the terms **base 3 cake** and **base 3 beverage** for the cake and the beverage in these two problems, and have a volunteer explain why we might use these terms. Ask students what they would call the cake and beverage in the original problem. They should see that the appropriate terms are *base 2 cake* and *base 2 beverage*.

Tell them that unless otherwise indicated, they should assume that the cake and beverage in "Alice problems" are base 2 cake and base 2 beverage. Also tell them that in any case, the beverage will always match the cake.

The graphs for Questions 3 and 4 will require even more difference in the scales than the graphs for Questions 1 and 2. You can have students express these functions in function notation, as was done with Questions 1 and 2.

- *Question 5*

There are several different comparisons that students can make in discussing Question 5. You can simply let volunteers share their observations and have the rest of the class comment.

The main observation is that in the "cake problems" (Questions 1 and 3), the $y$-value goes up rapidly as the $x$-value increases, while in the "beverage problems" (Questions 2 and 4), the $y$-value seems to get closer to 0 as the $x$-value increases. Students may also point out that the larger the base, the more extreme the change in $y$ as $x$ changes. That is, for the cake graphs, $y$ grows more rapidly if the base is larger, and for the beverage graphs, $y$ approaches 0 more rapidly if the base is larger.

- *Extending the graphs to the left*

***"Where would each graph cross the y-axis? What would happen as x became negative?"***

As a lead-in to later discussion of the use of zero and negative integers as exponents, have groups discuss where each graph would cross the $y$-axis and what each of the graphs might look like for negative inputs.

Both of these issues will be discussed later in the unit. (Zero as an exponent will be discussed on Days 3 and 4; negative exponents will be discussed on Days 6 through 8). These issues should be considered briefly at this point, too, but only in terms of what extending the graphs might suggest, not in terms of what zero or negative exponents might mean.

After a few minutes of discussion in groups, let volunteers share ideas. Students may see that all the graphs seem likely to cross the $y$-axis at the point (0, 1). They may also see that in the graphs from Questions 1 and 3, the $y$-values would seem likely to get closer to 0 as $x$ becomes "more negative," while in the graphs from Questions 2 and 4, the $y$-values would seem likely to get larger and larger as $x$ becomes "more negative."

- *Absolute growth versus percentage growth*

***"How does the effect on Alice's height of her third ounce of cake compare to the effect of her fifth ounce of cake?"***

Ask students to focus on the case of base 2 cake, and suggest that they have Alice start from a specific height, such as 5 feet. Then have them consider the effect on Alice's height of eating her third ounce of cake as compared to the effect of eating her fifth ounce of cake.

Using the starting height of 5 feet, they might see that the third ounce of cake increases Alice's height from 20 feet to 40 feet while the fifth ounce increases her height from 80 feet to 160 feet.

Bring out that although the latter is a larger increase (80 versus 20 feet of growth), both cases involve doubling Alice's height. Introduce the term **absolute growth** to refer to the numerical difference (found by subtracting the initial value from the final value) and the term **percentage growth** to refer to the proportional rate of increase (found by dividing the absolute growth by the initial value).

## Homework 2: A Wonderland Lost

Tonight's homework assignment gives students a chance to see a real-world context for the phenomenon of exponential decrease. This situation can be used tomorrow to reinforce the decision to define $x^0$ as 1.

# Homework 2 A Wonderland Lost

The Amazon rain forest is gradually being destroyed by pollution and agricultural and industrial development. Suppose, for simplicity, that each year, 10 percent of the remaining forest is destroyed. Assume for this assignment that the present area of the Amazon rain forest is 1,200,000 square miles.

1. a. What will the area of the forest be after one year of this destruction process?

   b. What will the area of the forest be after two years of the destruction process?

2. Make a graph showing your results from Question 1 and continuing through five years of the destruction process. Include the present situation as a point on your graph.

3. Find a rule for how much rain forest will remain after $X$ years. That is, express the area of the rain forest as a function of $X$.

4. Explain how this situation and its graph relate to Alice and her situation.

# Extending Exponentiation

The fundamental idea in Alice's adventure with the strange cake and beverage is that she grows and shrinks exponentially. Of course, the definition of exponentiation as repeated multiplication requires that the exponent be a positive whole number. But what if the exponent is zero? Or negative?

In the next portion of the unit, you'll use Alice's situation to gain insight into how the operation of exponentiation can be extended to allow these new types of exponents.

***This page in the student book introduces Days 3 through 8.***

***Erica Lanetot, Molly Jansen, Danielle Crisler, and Jillian Clark compare the results they got using the additive law of exponents.***

# Something Out of Nothing

*Students explore the meaning of zero as an exponent.*

## Mathematical Topics

- Working with exponential decrease
- Using zero as an exponent

## Outline of the Day

### In Class

1. Discuss *Homework 2: A Wonderland Lost*
   - Bring out that decreasing something by 10 percent is the same as multiplying it by 0.9
2. *Here Goes Nothing*
   - Students explore the meaning of zero as an exponent in several ways
3. Discuss *Here Goes Nothing*
   - Emphasize that the equation $2^0 = 1$ is a definition
4. Use the pattern of powers of 2 to reinforce the definition of $2^0$
5. Check on students' progress on *POW 14: More from Lewis Carroll*

### At Home

*Homework 3: A New Kind of Cake*

## Discuss With Your Colleagues

### Why Not Just Give Them the Definitions?

**Over the next several days, students will be gradually extending the definition of the operation of exponentiation to include zero, negative numbers, and fractions as exponents. Couldn't this be done a lot faster**

**simply by giving students the definitions? What are the pros and cons of the approach used in this unit? Are there parts of it that seem unnecessary?**

## 1. Discussion of *Homework 2: A Wonderland Lost*

You might begin by clarifying the fact that the 10 percent in the problem is always a percentage of the remaining forest, which decreases each year. One effective way to do this is to play devil's advocate, asking something like this:

> "If 10 percent of the forest is destroyed each year, how many years will it take until it is all gone? Ten years, right?"

Probably, most students will recognize that this statement is wrong. Getting a student who understands to explain why should clear up any possible confusion about the issue. (If needed, introduce a simpler specific area for the rain forest, such as 100,000 square miles, for students to work with.)

If this issue was a source of confusion to many students, you might let them take some time in their groups to reexamine the problem. Otherwise, simply have students report their results.

### • *Questions 1 and 2*

Let different diamond card students give the numerical results they got year by year for Questions 1 and 2, and have another diamond card student suggest scales for a graph of this information. Be sure to include the initial area given in the problem as the second coordinate for a point whose first coordinate is 0.

### • *Questions 3 and 4*

***"How does the area at the end of each year compare to the area at the beginning of that year?"***

Students may have had trouble developing a general rule for this situation, because repeatedly subtracting 10 percent does not lend itself to a simple expression. The key to obtaining a general rule is to recognize that decreasing something by 10 percent is the same as multiplying it by 0.9. You might ask how the amount left at the end of each year compares to the amount at the beginning of that year.

If this question doesn't help with the transition to multiplication, you can ask how this problem relates to the situation of Alice and her beverage. As a more directive hint, you can ask by what factor the area of the rain forest is multiplied each year. The relationship may be clearer if you have students look at a round number such as 100,000 square miles and then ask how the area after a year compares to the initial area.

In one way or another, students should be able to formulate the general expression $1{,}200{,}000 \cdot 0.9^X$ for the area after $X$ years. *Note:* Do not raise the question of why this rule works for $X = 0$ at this time. You will come back to that after the next activity.

No matter how students come up with the general rule, be sure to have them discuss how the rain-forest problem relates to Alice. Students should see that the homework situation is essentially the same as that of Alice and her beverage, except that Alice's height decreases by 50 percent per ounce while the rain forest decreases by 10 percent per year.

## 2. *Here Goes Nothing*

Before students begin this activity, you may want to review the formula developed yesterday that eating $C$ ounces of cake multiplies Alice's height by a factor of $2^C$.

On Question 3, you may need to clarify to groups that all they need to do is substitute 0 for $C$ in the expression $2^C$—they don't need to evaluate the expression. That is, they can simply write $2^0$ and stop there.

## 3. Discussion of *Here Goes Nothing*

You can begin by letting heart card students from different groups answer Questions 1 through 3. They should be clear that "eating 0 ounces of cake" doesn't change Alice's height, which means her height is multiplied by 1.

The presenter for Question 2 might refer to the posted graph (from Question 1 of *Homework 1: Graphing Alice*) and show that if the graph is continued to the left, it might hit the $y$-axis at $y = 1$. Although the graph might not point clearly to a $y$-value of 1, at this time students simply need to see that this result is reasonable.

On Question 3, they should see that substituting 0 for $C$ in the expression $2^C$ gives $2^0$. (As noted earlier, you may need to emphasize that they don't need to do anything more than this for Question 3.)

### • *Question 4*

Let volunteers respond to Question 4. You may need to summarize what the class concluded in Questions 1 through 3 so that the appropriate conclusion seems clear. The goal is to get the class to see that it seems to make sense for $2^0$ to be equal to 1.

### • *Back to the homework*

You can reinforce the discussion by returning to the graph from last night's homework. Remind students of the expression they found for the homework rain-forest situation ($1{,}200{,}000 \cdot 0.9^X$), and ask what value they want when $X = 0$. The graph should have included the point (0, 1,200,000), which shows that they want $1{,}200{,}000 \cdot 0.9^X$ to be equal to 1,200,000 when $X = 0$, which means that they want $0.9^0$ to be equal to 1.

### • *"$2^0 = 1$" is a definition*

It's very important for students to realize that a *definition* is needed in order to give meaning to the expression $2^0$. As needed, bring out that it makes sense to say that $2^3$ means to multiply three 2's together, or that $2^5$ means to multiply five 2's together, but it doesn't make sense to say that $2^0$ means to multiply zero 2's together. So a decision has to be made—that is, there needs to be a convention, an agreement—as to the value of $2^0$.

Tell students that long ago, mathematicians agreed to *define* $2^0$ as having a value of 1. Point out that the purpose of *Here Goes Nothing* is to show that this is the *most reasonable* definition, because it fits what happens to Alice and it fits the graph. You can inform them that in a moment, they will see another reason this definition makes sense.

*Note:* You can expect students both to resist and to forget this definition. The notion that any computation involving multiplication and zero gives a result of zero is a strong one, and it may take some students a while to let go of this idea.

## 4. The Exponential Pattern

The idea that $2^0 = 1$ should be reinforced by looking at the pattern of powers of 2. That is, make a list like this.

$$2^5 = 32$$

$$2^4 = 16$$

$$2^3 = 8$$

$$2^2 = 4$$

$$2^1 = 2$$

Get the class to articulate this pattern in various ways. For example, they might say, "Each result is twice the one below it," or "Divide by 2 as the exponent goes down by 1."

***"What would be the next equation in this pattern?"***

Ask the class what the next equation in this pattern would be. They should see that the natural way to continue this pattern is with the equation

$$2^0 = 1$$

Review with students the fact that $2^0 = 1$ is, ultimately, a definition. The usual definition of exponents in terms of repeated multiplication has broken down, because there are no 2's to multiply. Therefore, we must use some other method of defining the expression, and it makes sense to formulate the definition in a way that is consistent with other ideas.

You can ask the class to summarize the different reasons the definition "$2^0 = 1$" makes sense. They should identify at least three reasons.

- It fits the rule that $2^C$ tells what to multiply Alice's height by when she eats $C$ ounces of cake.

- It seems to be a reasonable way to extend what they already have of the graph of the equation $y = 2^x$.
- It fits the pattern of equations shown just discussed ($2^5 = 32, 2^4 = 16$, and so on).

As students see that all of these methods agree, they should become more satisfied with the definition. (Tomorrow, students will begin developing the additive law of exponents, and on Day 5, they will see that this law provides another way for justifying the definition.)

*Note:* In tonight's homework, students consider base 5 cake. Among other things, they are asked to give several explanations for why it makes sense to define $5^0$ as 1. *Homework 4: When Is Nothing Something?* continues this theme.

## 5. Progress Check on *POW 14: More from Lewis Carroll*

This is a good occasion to do a progress check of student work on *POW 14: More from Lewis Carroll.* One approach is to give students five or ten minutes in their groups to compare ideas, and then to take general questions. Another approach is to have students discuss the first problem or two either in their groups or as a whole class.

- ***More examples from Lewis Carroll***

You can use these additional examples to help students understand the POW.

a. No quadrupeds can whistle.

b. Some cats are quadrupeds.

(Possible conclusion: "Some cats can't whistle.")

a. All clever people are popular.

b. All obliging people are popular.

(No new conclusion.)

a. All puddings are nice.

b. This dish is a pudding.

c. No nice things are wholesome.

(Possible conclusion: "This dish is not wholesome.")

You may also want to let groups spend some time trying to make up problems of this type.

# Homework 3: A New Kind of Cake

Tonight's homework gives students a chance to check their grasp of using zero as an exponent. In Part II, they use a graph to explore the effect of switching base and exponent.

***In preparation for their homework, Darlene Cardenas, Elizabeth Diaz, and Jasmin Martinez verify the exponential pattern on their calculators.***

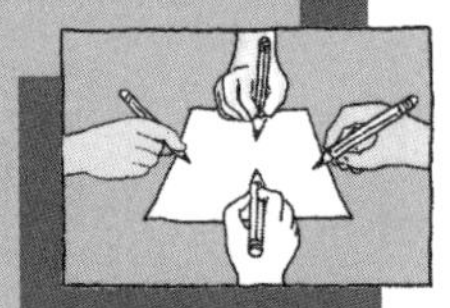



# Here Goes Nothing

For these problems, the cake Alice eats is base 2 cake, as in the original problem.

1. What would happen to Alice's height if she ate 0 ounces of cake? Specifically, what would her height be multiplied by?

2. In *Homework 1: Graphing Alice,* you made a graph of what Alice's height is multiplied by as a function of how much base 2 cake she eats. Examine that graph and explain whether your answer to Question 1 makes sense for that graph.

3. In *Alice in Wonderland,* you developed the general rule that eating $C$ ounces of base 2 cake multiplies Alice's height by $2^C$. According to this rule, what should Alice's height be multiplied by if she eats 0 ounces of this cake?

4. What does all this seem to point to as the value of $2^0$?

# Homework 3 A New Kind of Cake

## Part I: Base 5 Cake

Alice has discovered base 5 cake; that is, each ounce she eats of this cake multiplies her height by 5.

1. Figure out what Alice's height would be multiplied by if she ate 1 ounce, 2 ounces, 3 ounces, or 4 ounces of this cake.

2. Make a graph of your results from Question 1, using $x$ for the number of ounces Alice eats and $y$ for the number her height is multiplied by.

3. a. What would Alice's height be multiplied by if she ate 0 ounces of cake?

   b. Consider your answer to Question 3a in connection with your graph from Question 2. Does your answer to Question 3a seem to fit as a likely value for $y$ when $x$ is 0?

   c. Explain what Questions 3a and 3b have to do with defining $5^0$.

4. Use a pattern approach to explain why it makes sense to say $5^0 = 1$.

## Part II: Base or Exponent?

5. Graph the equations $y = 2^x$ and $y = x^2$ on the same set of axes. As $x$ gets big, which graph has the larger $y$-value? (Be sure to plot enough points to get a sense of the growth of each function.)

Students use the Alice metaphor to develop the additive law of exponents.

## Mathematical Topics

- Developing the additive law of exponents

## *Outline of the Day*

### In Class

1. Discuss *Homework 3: A New Kind of Cake*
   - Review ideas about zero as an exponent
2. *Piece After Piece*
   - Students use the Alice metaphor to develop the additive law of exponents
3. Discuss *Piece After Piece*
   - Have students use repeated multiplication to explain the additive law of exponents (for base 2)
4. Develop the general additive law of exponents

### At Home

*Homework 4: When Is Nothing Something?*

## 1. Discussion of *Homework 3: A New Kind of Cake*

The main purpose of Part I of *Homework 3: A New Kind of Cake* is for students to review the reasoning that leads to the definition of how zero is used as an exponent. You probably don't need to discuss Questions 1 and 2 explicitly, and so can go straight to Question 3.

You may want to have a volunteer present his or her ideas on this question. The presenter should note that eating 0 ounces multiplies Alice's height by 1 and that this does seem to fit the graph obtained in Question 2. (Because the scale on that graph covers such a wide range of values, this is not a very convincing argument for defining $5^0$ as 1.)

The key element of Question 3 is part c. The student might argue, for instance, that eating 2 ounces multiplies Alice's height by 25, which is $5^2$, and so eating 0 ounces should multiply Alice's height by $5^0$, which means $5^0$ must be equal to 1.

The presenter for Question 4 should be able to go through reasoning analogous to that done yesterday for powers of 2 to argue that it makes sense to define $5^0$ as 1.

- *Part II: Base or Exponent?*

Students presumably will have graphed the two equations by hand, plotting individual points. The main idea that needs to come out of this is the recognition that the expression $2^x$ grows much faster than the expression $x^2$ as $x$ gets big.

If students did not realize this, they probably did not go far enough out to the right with their graphs. You might have the class pick some numbers between 10 and 20 and find the values of both expressions, $2^x$ and $x^2$, for comparison.

You can also have students graph both equations on their graphing calculators and adjust the viewing rectangle so they see the comparison clearly.

*Comment:* The expressions $2^x$ and $x^2$ are equal when $x$ is 2 or 4, but $2^x$ is greater than $x^2$ when $x$ is greater than 4.

## 2. *Piece After Piece*

In the initial activity of the unit, *Alice in Wonderland,* students developed the principle that eating $C$ ounces of cake multiplies Alice's height by $2^C$. As noted on Day 2, this generalization depends on the assumption that eating $C$ ounces is the same as eating 1 ounce $C$ times. That is, we are assuming it doesn't matter whether Alice eats her cake all at once or one ounce at a time.

In the next activity, *Piece After Piece,* students will use this assumption to develop the additive law of exponents.

No introduction is needed for this activity. Have students work on it in groups, and then discuss it immediately afterward.

# 3. Discussion of *Piece After Piece*

***If the answer for Question 1a is that Alice's height is multiplied by 256, ask: "What are the stages of her height change?"***

You can begin by having spade card students answer Questions 1a and 1b. The presenter for Question 1a might simply describe what happens overall, saying something like, "Her height is multiplied by 256." If so, ask for an explanation of how the presenter arrived at this conclusion. Try to get the student to explain that Alice's height is multiplied first by 8 and then by 32. Bring out that 8 comes from the expression $2^3$ and that 32 comes from the expression $2^5$.

***"If Alice's initial height is h, and she eats 3 ounces of cake, what will her new height be?"***

If students have trouble getting started, you might suggest that they represent Alice's original height with a variable such as $h$ (or perhaps using a specific numerical value). You can then ask, "If Alice eats 3 ounces of cake, what will her new height be?" You can write the response from the students as $h \cdot 2^3$. You can proceed similarly with the second stage, writing the next result as $(h \cdot 2^3) \cdot 2^5$, and then ask a similar question for 8 ounces.

***"How does the arithmetic explain why the results are the same?"***

If students tried a specific initial height for Alice, they will certainly see that the overall result is the same as eating 8 ounces of cake. Focus on the explanation for this in terms of the arithmetic, trying to get students to say something like, "Multiplying by 8 and then by 32 is the same as multiplying by 256."

The goal here is to bring out what this means in terms of expressions with exponents. Essentially, it says that $2^3 \cdot 2^5$ is the same as $2^8$. (Actually, the associative property is also involved here, but don't get sidetracked by that.)

This fact may seem obvious to some students, but not to others. A good way to clarify the relationship is to make the individual factors of 2 explicit by asking students where the factor of 8 comes from, for instance. Go back to the expression $2^3$, and ask them to break this down into individual factors—that is, as $2 \cdot 2 \cdot 2$.

Proceeding similarly with the factor $2^5$, they should see that $2^3 \cdot 2^5$ can be written as

$$(2 \cdot 2 \cdot 2) \cdot (2 \cdot 2 \cdot 2 \cdot 2 \cdot 2)$$

At the same time, they should see that the single expression $2^8$ is equal to

$$2 \cdot 2 \cdot 2 \cdot 2 \cdot 2 \cdot 2 \cdot 2 \cdot 2$$

***"How many 2's are in the expression $2 \cdot 2 \cdot 2$? In $2 \cdot 2 \cdot 2 \cdot 2 \cdot 2$? In $2 \cdot 2 \cdot 2 \cdot 2 \cdot 2 \cdot 2 \cdot 2 \cdot 2$?"***

You can ask about the number of 2's in each expression and then go back to the exponential forms of these expressions to develop the equation

$$2^3 \cdot 2^5 = 2^8$$

Once you have this equation with exponential expressions, you can go back to the individual 2's again, writing the equation as

$$(2 \cdot 2 \cdot 2) \cdot (2 \cdot 2 \cdot 2 \cdot 2 \cdot 2) = 2 \cdot 2 \cdot 2 \cdot 2 \cdot 2 \cdot 2 \cdot 2 \cdot 2$$

- *Question 2*

This is a good time to interrupt the development and look at some other examples. You can ask for volunteers to describe what they did on Question 2 of the assignment and do a brief version of the development above for one or two examples.

If you get examples with small exponents, you can have students write out the individual factors, getting expressions like this:

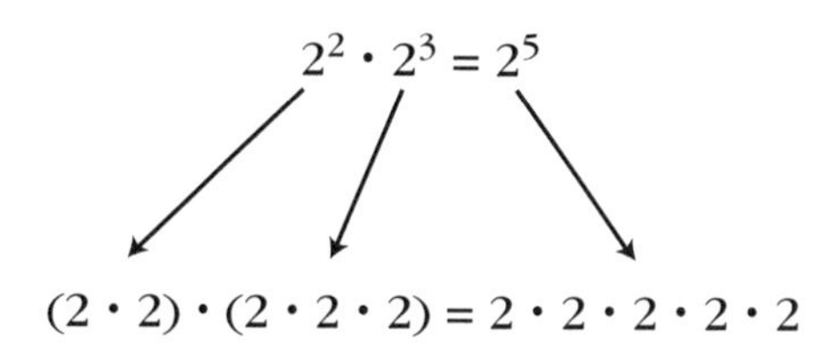


You can move from examples like this one, in which students can actually count the factors, to examples in which they simply add the exponents, such as

$$2^{17} \cdot 2^{32} = 2^{49}$$

Finally, ask for a generalization of this process. Students will probably be able to develop an equation such as

$$2^X \cdot 2^Y = 2^{X+Y}$$

*Note:* Because the letters *B* and *C* are used in this unit to refer to numbers of ounces of beverage and cake, respectively, you should probably avoid them in this context.

- *Question 3*

Before going on to the general additive law of exponents, have a volunteer present Question 3. If it doesn't come up in the presentation, ask explicitly how the reasoning would apply if the situation were about beverage instead of cake.

Students should be able to develop a "beverage counterpart" to the last equation along the lines of

$$\left(\frac{1}{2}\right)^X \cdot \left(\frac{1}{2}\right)^Y = \left(\frac{1}{2}\right)^{X+Y}$$

# 4. The Additive Law of Exponents

As an additional stage in the development of the general additive law of exponents, you can ask students to make up similar examples of what would happen if Alice had another type of cake.

*As a hint:*
*"Does eating 3 ounces and then 5 ounces of base 7 cake have the same effect as eating 8 ounces? Why?"*

If they need prompting, you might ask for an equation showing why the result of eating 3 ounces of base 7 cake and then 5 ounces of that cake is the same as eating 8 ounces of it. Students should be able to explain this with an expression such as

$$\underbrace{(7 \cdot 7 \cdot 7)}_{\text{3 factors}} \cdot \underbrace{(7 \cdot 7 \cdot 7 \cdot 7 \cdot 7)}_{\text{5 factors}}$$

pointing out that this gives a total of 8 factors, so $7^3 \cdot 7^5$ is equal to $7^8$.

Depending on how your students respond, you might go directly from such examples to the most general case, or you might have them develop generalizations for specific bases other than 2. For example, they might come up with the equation

$$7^X \cdot 7^Y = 7^{X+Y}$$

Students should be able to generalize all this into the principle

$$A^X \cdot A^Y = A^{X+Y}$$

*"What does $A^X$ mean? What does $A^Y$ mean? How would you write these expressions without using exponents?"*

You can help them understand this more visually by asking a series of questions that leads them to express each exponential expression as a product of a group of factors. You can match the individual exponential expressions with their "written out" forms to get a display like this one.

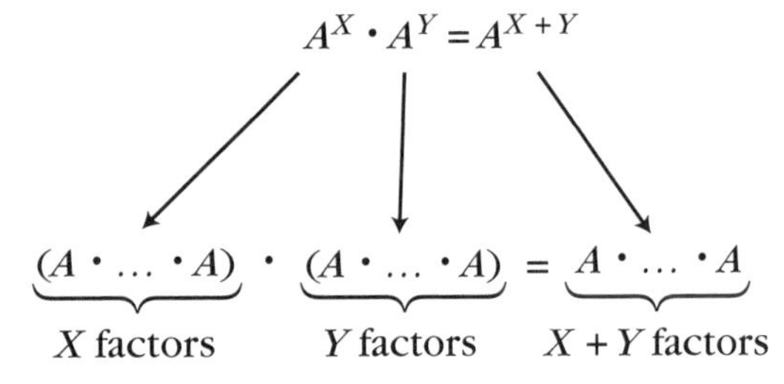


Identify the generalization $A^X \cdot A^Y = A^{X+Y}$ as the **additive law of exponents.** Point out that it involves a situation in which these two things hold true:

- The bases are the same.
- The two exponential expressions are being multiplied.

Post the additive law of exponents together with the displayed "explanation." Stress its importance to students, and tell them many other important facts about exponents can be derived both from this law itself and from the type of reasoning used to develop it.

## Homework 4: When Is Nothing Something?

In this assignment, students focus on the special meaning of zero as an exponent.

# *Piece After Piece*

Alice does not always eat her cake in one sitting. At times, she eats some cake, follows a rabbit for a while, and then comes back and eats some more cake. In this activity, you investigate what happens to Alice's height when she eats piece after piece of cake. (Assume that she has the original base 2 cake.)

1. Suppose Alice eats a 3-ounce piece of cake, takes a break, and then later eats a 5-ounce piece of cake.
   a. What happens to her height?
   b. Is the result the same as if she had eaten a single 8-ounce piece of the cake? Explain.
2. Make up two more pairs of questions like those in Question 1. Answer them and explain your reasoning.
3. Now answer Questions 1 and 2 as if they were about the beverage instead of about the cake.

# Homework 4 When Is Nothing Something?

Clarabell says:

"The number 0 stands for nothing. So $3^0$ means no 3's. No 3's is zero, so $3^0$ equals 0."

Bellaclar says:

"The number 0 stands for nothing. So $3^0$ is the same as a 3 with no exponent, and that's just 3. Therefore, $3^0$ equals 3."

1. Explain to Clarabell and Bellaclar why $3^0$ is not equal to 0 or to 3.

2. Here are two situations in which the number 0 is *not* nothing.

   - Example 1: The 0 in 20 is not nothing, because otherwise there would be no difference between 2 and 20.
   - Example 2: A temperature of 0 degrees is not the same as there not being any temperature (whatever that means).

   Make up two more situations in which 0 is *not* nothing.

3. Mathematicians have decided that it makes sense to define $3^0$ (and expressions like it) as equal to 1. They saw that this definition fits well with other principles about exponents, and so it makes working with exponents logical.

   When people agree to use a word or symbol in a particular way, such an agreement is called a **convention.** Think back on other mathematical topics you have studied, and write about another situation in which you think a *convention* is involved.

DAY 5

# Many Meals for Alice

*Students get another perspective on zero as an exponent and find a new law of exponents.*

## Mathematical Topics

- Using the additive law of exponents to explain the use of zero as an exponent
- Developing the law of repeated exponentiation

## Outline of the Day

### In Class

1. Discuss *Homework 4: When Is Nothing Something?*
2. Using the additive law of exponents to explain zero as an exponent
3. *Many Meals for Alice*
   - Students examine what happens if Alice eats several meals of the same size
4. Discuss *Many Meals for Alice*
   - Bring out the general law $(A^D)^M = A^{DM}$

### At Home

*Homework 5: In Search of the Law*

## 1. Discussion of *Homework 4: When Is Nothing Something?*

Have several volunteers give their explanations for Question 1. It's fine if they focus on why Clarabell and Bellaclar are wrong, rather than on why $3^0$ is actually defined to be 1.

Questions 2 and 3 give students an opportunity to be both imaginative and reflective. There is no specific mathematical content that needs to come out of these questions, so you can let the discussion be shaped by what students have to offer.

## 2. Zero as an Exponent in the Additive Law of Exponents

***"How could you use $2^0$ in the additive law of exponents?"***

If it hasn't yet come up, ask students to work with $2^0$ in the additive law of exponents. That is, ask them to give you an instance of the additive law of exponents that uses $2^0$. (If they need clarification of what you want, you can tell them that $2^5 \cdot 2^7 = 2^{12}$ is an instance of the additive law of exponents that uses $2^7$, and that they need to think up an instance using $2^0$.)

Suppose, for example, they give you the equation

$$2^0 \cdot 2^3 = 2^3$$

***"What number does $2^0$ act like in this equation?"***

Ask what number $2^0$ acts like in this equation. To clarify this question, you can show each $2^3$ in the equation replaced by the number 8 and $2^0$ replaced by a box, as shown below. You may want to pose the specific question, "What number should be put in the box to give a true equation?"

$$2^0 \cdot 2^3 = 2^3$$

$$\downarrow \quad \downarrow \quad \downarrow$$

$$\square \cdot 8 = 8$$

Students should see that they need the number 1 in the box, so $2^0$ is acting like 1 in the equation $2^0 \cdot 2^3 = 2^3$.

Bring out that this analysis based on the additive law of exponents is yet another reason to define $2^0$ as 1. Emphasize that this is consistent with what they have already seen, based on three things.

- Alice eating no cake
- The graph of $y = 2^x$
- The pattern of exponential values

## 3. *Many Meals for Alice*

The next activity, *Many Meals for Alice,* gives students a chance to develop another general law about exponents. This law deals with expressions of the form $(a^b)^c$.

You may want to suggest specific other examples to groups that are having trouble generalizing from Question 2.

The main idea of this activity can be brought out based on students' work with Question 2; Questions 3 through 5 are mainly for faster groups. You may want to wait until all groups have at least begun work on Question 3 before starting presentations.

# 4. Discussion of *Many Meals for Alice*

Have club card students from one or two different groups give their results for Questions 1 and 2.

Students will probably express their answers to Question 1 as powers of 8 (because each meal multiplies Alice's height by $2^3$, or 8). In general, this gives $8^M$ as the multiplying factor for $M$ meals of 3 ounces each.

For the general expression in Question 2, they will probably replace 8 by $2^D$ and get $(2^D)^M$ as the factor by which her height is multiplied after $M$ meals with $D$ ounces of cake at each meal.

***"How much cake was eaten altogether? What does that do to Alice's height?"***

A second approach for Question 2 is to recognize that Alice is eating a total of $DM$ ounces of cake, so her height is multiplied by $2^{DM}$. If no one uses this second approach, you can ask questions such as "How much cake was eaten altogether?" and "What does that do to Alice's height?" If you ask these questions for Question 1, you should get answers of "$3M$ ounces" and "multiply by $2^{3M}$." For Question 2, the answers would be "$DM$ ounces" and "multiply by $2^{DM}$."

The key idea of the activity is to compare the two expressions $(2^D)^M$ and $2^{DM}$. Because students have established the general principle that the sequence in which the cake is eaten doesn't matter, comparing the two methods gives

$$(2^D)^M = 2^{DM}$$

***"Will this rule work with bases other than 2?"***

You can ask whether this rule would work if the base were something other than 2. Students will probably not have trouble generalizing this to

$$(A^D)^M = A^{DM}$$

### • *Explaining the formula*

***"Can you write the process as a long multiplication problem?"***

Once students have developed the general formula $(A^D)^M = A^{DM}$, ask them to explain the process in terms of repeated multiplication. You can use a sequence of equalities such as the following to connect the two sides of the general equation:

$$
\begin{aligned}
(A^D)^M &= \underbrace{(A^D \cdot A^D \cdot \ldots \cdot A^D)}_{M \text{ factors}} \\
&= \underbrace{\underbrace{(A \cdot A \cdot \ldots \cdot A)}_{D \text{ factors}} \cdot \underbrace{(A \cdot A \cdot \ldots \cdot A)}_{D \text{ factors}} \cdot \ldots \cdot \underbrace{(A \cdot A \cdot \ldots \cdot A)}_{D \text{ factors}}}_{M \text{ groups}} \\
&= \underbrace{A \cdot A \cdot A \cdot \ldots \cdot A}_{DM \text{ factors altogether}} \\
&= A^{DM}
\end{aligned}
$$

The general formula

$$(A^D)^M = A^{DM}$$

can be posted, with an explanation like that above, and labeled as the **law of repeated exponentiation.**

### • *Questions 3 through 5*

If time allows, use Questions 3 through 5 to develop the rule

$$(2^D)^M = (2^M)^D$$

## *Homework 5: In Search of the Law*

Tonight's homework is a follow-up to the activity *Many Meals for Alice.* It asks students to investigate other situations with exponents and to develop other general principles. In *Homework 11: Confusion Reigns,* we ask students to reexamine these general principles so that they don't simply memorize rules.

# Many Meals for Alice

Alice has decided that she will be healthier if she eats fewer sweets. Therefore, she will eat a fixed number of ounces of cake each time she sits down for a meal.

Your task is to find out what would happen to her height after different numbers of meals with a given amount of cake. (Alice is eating base 2 cake in these problems.)

1. Suppose Alice decides that she will eat 3 ounces of cake at each meal. What will her height be multiplied by after two meals? After three meals? After four meals? After $M$ meals?

2. Experiment with different amounts of cake at each meal and different numbers of meals. Use your examples to develop an expression for what her height will be multiplied by after $M$ meals with $D$ ounces of cake at each meal.

3. Would eating 4 ounces of cake at each of six meals be the same as eating 6 ounces of cake at each of four meals? Why or why not?

4. Make up another example like Question 3. Your example should compare two situations in which you switch the number of ounces with the number of meals.

5. Write a general law of exponents that expresses your observations from Questions 3 and 4.

# Homework 5 — In Search of the Law

You have seen that if you multiply two exponential expressions with the same base, such as $2^3$ and $2^5$, the product is an expression such as $2^8$, where the base is the same as before and the exponent is the sum of the exponents from the factors.

This principle is called the **additive law of exponents** and can be expressed by the general equation

$$A^X \cdot A^Y = A^{X+Y}$$

Actually, there are many laws that relate to exponents. In this assignment, you'll investigate other possible laws.

1. Suppose the exponential expressions being multiplied have different bases but the same exponent. That is, consider products of the form $A^X \cdot B^X$. Look for a general law for simplifying such products. As needed, examine specific cases, such as $3^7 \cdot 5^7$, using the definition of exponentiation to write this expression as a product of 3's and 5's.

2. Suppose the two factors have the same base *and* the same exponent. Do you apply the additive law of exponents or do you use your answer to Question 1? Look at specific cases to investigate what to do with expressions of the form $A^X \cdot A^X$.

3. A common mistake people make when working with exponents is to multiply the base by the exponent instead of raising the base to the power of the exponent. For instance, they would mistakenly say that $2^3$ is 6 (because $2 \cdot 3 = 6$) when the correct answer is actually 8 (because $2 \cdot 2 \cdot 2 = 8$).

   Are there any pairs of numbers for which this mistake in thinking actually gives the correct answer? In other words, are there any solutions to the equation $A^X = A \cdot X$? If so, what are they?

DAY 6

# Having Your Cake and Drinking Too

*Students continue using the Alice metaphor to develop laws of exponents.*

## Mathematical Topics

- Developing more laws of exponents
- Preparing to work with negative exponents

## *Outline of the Day*

### In Class

1. Discuss *Homework 5: In Search of the Law*
   - Bring out the principle $A^X \cdot B^X = (A \cdot B)^X$
2. *Having Your Cake and Drinking Too*
   - Students look at what happens to Alice if she combines cake and beverage
   - The activity will be discussed on Day 7

### At Home

*Homework 6: Rallods in Rednow Land*

## 1. Discussion of *Homework 5: In Search of the Law*

Let students compare ideas briefly in groups, and then have diamond card students from different groups report. The focus should be on having students explain what's happening with the factors involved in a given exponential expression. In the long run, having students understand specific examples will be more productive than having them memorize formulas.

## • *Question 1*

In Question 1, students should see how to regroup and pair the factors. If the presenter doesn't bring this out clearly, you can prod for specifics.

***"How would you write $3^7 \cdot 5^7$ as repeated multiplication?"***

For instance, suppose the presenter is working with the specific example $3^7 \cdot 5^7$ as given in the problem. You can ask how these two expressions would be written as repeated multiplication, which should give the expression

$$3 \cdot 3 \cdot 3 \cdot 3 \cdot 3 \cdot 3 \cdot 3 \cdot 5 \cdot 5 \cdot 5 \cdot 5 \cdot 5 \cdot 5 \cdot 5$$

***"How can you use the fact that there are the same number of 3's as 5's?"***

You can then ask how to use the fact that there are the same number of 3's as 5's. Bring out that this allows the factors to be rearranged and paired up, as shown here.

$$(3 \cdot 5) \cdot (3 \cdot 5) \cdot (3 \cdot 5) \cdot (3 \cdot 5) \cdot (3 \cdot 5) \cdot (3 \cdot 5) \cdot (3 \cdot 5)$$

This shows that the expression $3^7 \cdot 5^7$ can be rewritten as $(3 \cdot 5)^7$.

If needed, have another student present a similar example, and work toward a generalization of the principle. Students should see that any product of the form $A^X \cdot B^X$ can be simplified as

$$A^X \cdot B^X = (A \cdot B)^X$$

You may want to ask students to explain this general principle in terms of repeated multiplication in a manner similar to that used for the specific examples. For example, a display like this illustrates the method of rearranging and regrouping the factors. Post this principle with its explanation.

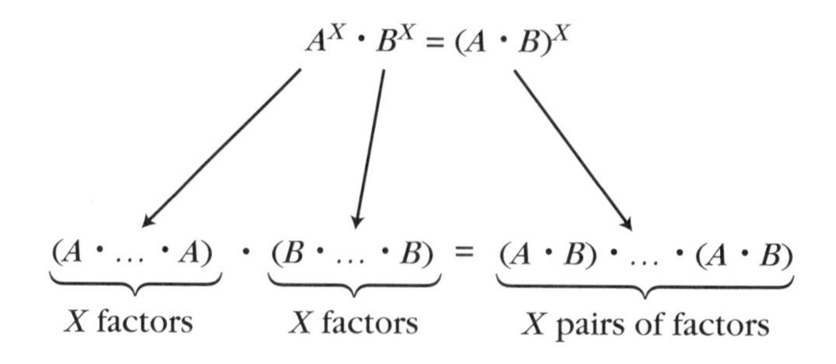


## • *Question 2*

The goal in Question 2 is to bring out that an expression such as $A^X \cdot A^X$ can be simplified using either the principle from Question 1 or the additive law of exponents, and that the two methods give equivalent results. In the course of the discussion you can review a principle explored yesterday in *Many Meals for Alice.*

According to the additive law of exponents, $A^X \cdot A^X$ is equal to $A^{X+X}$, which equals $A^{2X}$. By the principle from Question 1, $A^X \cdot A^X$ is equal to $(A \cdot A)^X$, which equals $(A^2)^X$. But by the principle from *Many Meals for Alice,* $(A^2)^X$ is equal to $A^{2X}$. Thus the two approaches—the additive law of exponents and the principle from Question 1—ultimately lead to the same answer.

- *Question 3*

*Note:* This problem is tangential to the main unit, so you can omit discussion if time is short, and you need not push for a solution.

Let students share their results on Question 3. It turns out that the only *positive integer* solutions to the equation $A^X = A \cdot X$ are

- $X = 1$ and $A$ = any number
- $X = 2$ and $A = 2$

However, you should also ask students to consider the case in which $A$ is equal to 0. They should see that as long as $X$ is positive, both sides come out equal to 0.

- *What about $0^0$?*

The case of Question 3 for which $X$ and $A$ are both 0 presents a special problem. Bring out that in trying to define $0^0$, there is a contradiction between two principles.

- On the one hand, any power of 0 ought to be equal to 0.
- On the other hand, we've defined expressions with an exponent of 0 to be equal to 1.

(You may need to look at examples such as $0^2$, $0^3$, and so on to clarify the first principle.)

Because of this contradiction, the expression $0^0$ is generally considered undefined. (Calculators give an error message if you try to find $0^0$.)

***"Do you know of any other situations in which operations are undefined?"***

Ask students if they know of any other situations in which operations are undefined. If no one thinks of any, then you should remind them of division by zero and discuss why expressions like $5 \div 0$ are undefined.

*Note:* The issue of undefined expressions will come up again when negative exponents are considered.

## 2. *Having Your Cake and Drinking Too*

The goal of the next activity, *Having Your Cake and Drinking Too,* is to have students discover why it makes sense to define expressions using negative exponents—expressions such as $2^{-3}$—as representing fractions.

Allow enough time so that all groups can at least start Question 4. The activity is scheduled for discussion tomorrow, and you may want to give students more time to work on it tomorrow before the discussion.

If a group's expression for Question 4 is

$$2^C \cdot \left(\frac{1}{2}\right)^B$$

encourage the members to look at their examples from Question 1 in order to find a way to write this answer as a power of 2 with a single exponent.

Question 5 is included in the activity to provide interesting work for faster groups. If individual groups don't get to it, you can deal with the issue it raises in tomorrow's whole-class discussion.

## *Homework 6: Rallods in Rednow Land*

Tonight's homework presents students with a classic problem in exponential growth.

***During an IMP Year 2 inservice, Judy Strauss and Dave Robathan discuss exponential growth.***

# Having Your Cake and Drinking Too

You have found that the additive law of exponents gives an easy way to calculate what happens to Alice when she eats several pieces of cake. For example, the equation below shows how to combine the effect of a 17-ounce piece of base 2 cake with that of a 5-ounce piece of that cake.

$$2^{17} \cdot 2^5 = 2^{17+5} = 2^{22}$$

You also found out how to combine several servings of the beverage. For example, here is an equation that shows how to combine the effect of a 4-ounce serving of base 2 beverage with that of a 9-ounce serving of that beverage.

$$\left(\frac{1}{2}\right)^4 \cdot \left(\frac{1}{2}\right)^9 = \left(\frac{1}{2}\right)^{4+9} = \left(\frac{1}{2}\right)^{13}$$

*Continued on next page*



How does this work with Alice's Height?

In this activity, your goal is to figure out how to determine the effect on Alice of combining base 2 cake and base 2 beverage.

1. What is Alice's height multiplied by if she consumes the same number of ounces of cake and beverage? Write an equation using exponential expressions that expresses your answer.
2. Write at least five ways to combine eating cake with drinking beverage that will result in Alice being 8 times her original height. That is, find combinations of amounts of cake and of beverage for which her original height will be multiplied by $2^3$.
3. a. Find several combinations of amounts of cake and beverage that will result in Alice being 32 times her original height.

   b. Find several combinations of amounts of cake and beverage that will result in Alice being 4 times her original height.
4. Look for a pattern in your answers to Questions 2 and 3. Write a general expression for the amount Alice's height is multiplied by if she eats $C$ ounces of cake and drinks $B$ ounces of beverage.
5. What happens to your rule in Question 4 if $B$ is more than $C$?

$2^2 \cdot \frac{1}{2}^2$

$4 \cdot \frac{1}{4} = 1$

$2^5 \cdot \frac{1}{2}^5 =$

$2^0$

$2^3 \cdot \frac{1}{2}^0 = 8$

$2^5 \cdot \frac{1}{2}^2 = 8$

$2^5 \cdot 2^{-2} = 2^3 = 8$

planting seed for subtracting exp

$A^x \cdot B^x = (A \cdot B)^x$

$2^x \cdot \frac{1}{2}^y$

$2^{x-y}$

5+7

What is happening with Alice's height when she drinks the beverage?

What if I wanted to keep the bases the same how could I we write ½ ~~as a~~ with 2 as the base

$2^{-1}$

# Homework 6 Rallods in Rednow Land

The ruler of Rednow Land had a very wise advisor who had saved the country in various ways (such as finding counterfeiters of gold coins). The ruler wanted to reward this wise person.

The ruler loved to play chess and so came up with two choices of rewards for the wise advisor.

- Choice A: A billion rallods (a rallod is the coin of Rednow Land)
- Choice B: The amount of money obtained by putting 1 rallod on one square of the chessboard, 2 rallods on the next, 4 on the next, 8 on the next, and so on until all 64 squares were filled

1. What does your intuition tell you about which would be the better choice?
2. Now make a decision based on the results of computation. Explain your decision.
3. The standard chessboard has 64 squares. How many squares would be needed to make Choice B as close as possible to Choice A? Explain your reasoning.

*Historical note:* This assignment is an adaptation of a problem that can be traced to Persia in about the seventh century and that may have originated even earlier in India.

# Day 7 Negative Exponents

*Students use the Alice metaphor to define expressions with negative exponents.*

## Mathematical Topics

- Appreciating the power of exponential growth
- Defining expressions with negative exponents

## *Outline of the Day*

### In Class

1. Discuss *Homework 6: Rallods in Rednow Land*
   - Bring out that exponential expressions grow very quickly
2. Discuss *Having Your Cake and Drinking Too* (from Day 6)
   - Have students use examples to develop the formula that eating $C$ ounces of cake and drinking $B$ ounces of beverage multiplies Alice's height by $2^{C-B}$
3. Defining negative exponents
   - Substitute 0 for $C$ in the expression $2^{C-B}$ to see that it makes sense to define $2^{-B}$ as $\frac{1}{2^B}$

### At Home

*Homework 7: Continuing the Pattern*

## 1. Discussion of *Homework 6: Rallods in Rednow Land*

*Note:* Students may have encountered scientific notation on their calculators in their work on this assignment. Though some students may have seen this idea before (for instance, in science class), others may not be familiar with it at all. If students raise questions about "strange" results on their calculators, you can give a brief explanation and tell them that they will learn more about this later in the unit.

The main goal in this homework is for students to feel the power of exponential growth, that is, for them to see how quickly powers grow.

On Question 1, you may want to point out that many of us don't have very good intuition about dealing with large exponents, because we don't have much experience with them. Help students to realize that there is no "right answer" for a question that asks them about their intuition.

You may want to give groups a few minutes to compare notes on Question 2 and then have a heart card student report. Students do not need to find the sum of the sequence $1 + 2 + 4 + \cdots + 2^{63}$ in order to answer Question 2, because the thirty-first square by itself already has more than a billion rallods.

You can have another heart card student or two report on Question 3. One approach is to keep on adding terms until the sum reaches 1 billion. Another approach is to recognize that each term is 1 more than the sum of the previous terms and then look for a term that is over half a billion. A third approach is to look at the two or three biggest terms and assume that this will be close enough. All of these approaches will show that 30 squares give just over a billion rallods.

*Note:* The supplemental problem *More About Rallods* asks students to find a general formula for the sum of the first $n$ powers of 2.

## 2. Discussion of *Having Your Cake and Drinking Too*

If necessary, allow students some more time to work on yesterday's activity. You can begin the discussion after all the groups have done some work on Question 4.

Begin the discussion with Question 1, getting students to articulate the idea that equal amounts of cake and beverage "cancel out." They may be able to write a general equation such as

$$2^N \cdot \left(\frac{1}{2}\right)^N = 1$$

to explain this cancellation, but it isn't necessary that they express the idea so formally.

- *Questions 2 and 3*

Next, move on to Question 2. Students should see that any combination in which the number of ounces of cake is 3 more than the number of ounces of beverage will work here. They should find similar results for the two parts of Question 3.

***"How do you get from the number of ounces of cake and beverage to the effect on Alice's height?"***

Questions 2 and 3 started with a desired result and asked for combinations that yielded that result. But through their work on these questions, students will probably have seen how to go in the other direction. Ask them to articulate the arithmetic they do when presented with a combination of cake and beverage. For example, they might say, "Subtract the number of ounces of beverage from the number of ounces of cake, and take 2 to that power."

## • *Question 4*

***"If C is the number of ounces of cake and B is the number of ounces of beverage, what happens to Alice's height?"***

Ask students to express their observations about individual cases as a general formula. For example, have them use $C$ as the number of ounces of cake and $B$ as the number of ounces of beverage. They should be able to state that Alice's height gets multiplied by $2^{C-B}$.

You may want to ask for an equation that shows the two separate effects (of the cake and the beverage) being combined into a single expression. For example, a student might write

$$2^C \cdot \left(\frac{1}{2}\right)^B = 2^{C-B}$$

(If no one sees this quickly, you can move on and perhaps come back to it later.)

Before going on, you should post the expression $2^{C-B}$ for combining cake and beverage, because students will be referring to it as the basis for defining negative exponents.

## • *Reinforcing the formula*

***"Does the expression $2^{C-B}$ work if B and C are equal?"***

It is important to build confidence in the expression $2^{C-B}$, because the next topic is to use this expression to motivate the definition of negative exponents. You can build this confidence, and at the same time reinforce earlier work with zero as an exponent, by asking if the expression works when $B$ and $C$ are equal. (You may want to use a specific example related to the Alice metaphor, such as Alice eating 4 ounces of cake and then washing it down with 4 ounces of beverage.)

Students should see that if $B$ is equal to $C$, then Alice's height doesn't change, so it is multiplied by 1. Because the expression gives $2^{4-4}$ and we have defined $2^0$ to be equal to 1, the expression does work when $B$ is equal to $C$.

## • *Question 5*

The discussion of Question 5 is implicit in the introduction to negative exponents described next, so no separate discussion is needed.

## 3. Negative Exponents

***"What does the formula say about the case in which Alice eats 0 ounces of cake and drinks 3 ounces of beverage?"***

To introduce the idea of negative exponents, ask what the expression $2^{C-B}$ says in the cases in which $B$ is greater than $C$. It's best to start with specific cases. For example, ask what happens if Alice eats 0 ounces of cake and drinks 3 ounces of beverage.

There are two aspects to this question, and the key is bringing them together.

- Drinking 3 ounces of beverage multiplies Alice's height by $\left(\frac{1}{2}\right)^3$, which is $\frac{1}{8}$.
- Substituting 0 for $C$ and 3 for $B$ in the expression $2^{C-B}$ gives that Alice's height is multiplied by $2^{0-3}$, which can be simplified as $2^{-3}$.

(You may need to ask leading questions to get both ideas from the class.)

Once both aspects of the problem have come out, ask students what this tells them about defining $2^{-3}$. You may want to remind them that, like $2^0$, the expression $2^{-3}$ cannot be defined in the usual way, that is, in terms of repeated multiplication.

Students' work in developing the definition of $2^0$ will probably lead them to conclude that it makes sense to define $2^{-3}$ as $\frac{1}{8}$. (At least it makes sense in terms of the Alice metaphor. In tonight's homework, students will see a different approach to the same conclusion.)

***"How can you generalize these results? How should we define $2^{-B}$?"***

Present students with one or two more numerical examples, and then ask them to generalize the results using $B$ for the number of ounces of beverage. On the one hand, this formula tells them to multiply Alice's height by $2^{0-B}$, which is $2^{-B}$. On the other hand, they know from Day 2 that drinking $B$ ounces of beverage (while eating no cake) will multiply Alice's height by $\frac{1}{2^B}$.

Thus, they should see that for the sake of consistency, it makes sense to *define* $2^{-B}$ as $\frac{1}{2^B}$. *Note:* If students prefer to use $\left(\frac{1}{2}\right)^B$ instead of $\frac{1}{2^B}$, that's fine.

As with the zero exponent, emphasize that this is a definition.

## *Homework 7: Continuing the Pattern*

This homework will give students another way of thinking about the fact that negative exponents (with whole-number bases) give fractional values.

# Homework 7 Continuing the Pattern

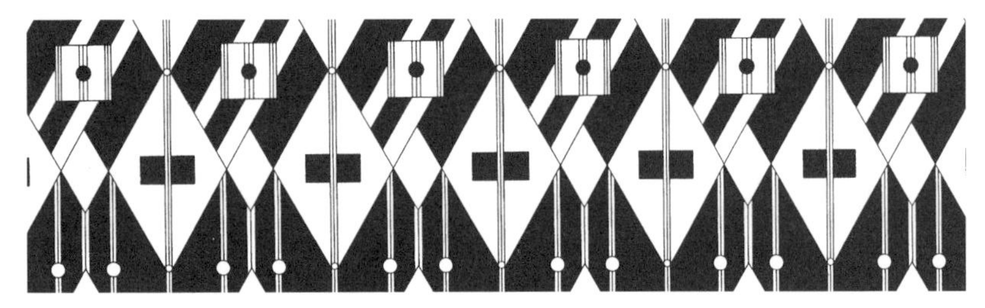

*Closeup of an Art Deco design from "Original Art Deco Allover Patterns," copyright © 1989 by Dover Publications, Inc.*

You've seen several different ways to explain the definition of $2^0$ as 1. In this assignment, you'll adapt one of those methods to think about defining exponential expressions using negative exponents.

1. Begin by examining the powers of 2 shown here.

$$2^5 = 32$$
$$2^4 = 16$$
$$2^3 = 8$$
$$2^2 = 4$$
$$2^1 = 2$$
$$2^0 = 1$$
$$2^{-1} = ?$$
$$2^{-2} = ?$$
$$2^{-3} = ?$$
$$2^{-4} = ?$$

   a. Describe the pattern of numerical values shown on the right sides of these equations for powers of 2 with positive and zero exponents.

   b. Explain how you would use this pattern to find the missing values for powers of 2 with negative exponents. Express your numerical results *as fractions* (not as decimals).

*Continued on next page*



emphasize what is happening to Alice as she drinks

2. a. Make similar lists for powers of 3 and powers of 5 using positive and zero exponents, and extend these lists to negative exponents.

   b. Describe how your results for these lists compare with your results on Question 1.

3. If the base is $\frac{1}{2}$, the list of powers for positive exponents looks like this.

$$\left(\frac{1}{2}\right)^5 = \frac{1}{32}$$

$$\left(\frac{1}{2}\right)^4 = \frac{1}{16}$$

$$\left(\frac{1}{2}\right)^3 = \frac{1}{8}$$

$$\left(\frac{1}{2}\right)^2 = \frac{1}{4}$$

$$\left(\frac{1}{2}\right)^1 = \frac{1}{2}$$

$$\left(\frac{1}{2}\right)^0 = 1$$

Extend this list to negative exponents, and compare your results with your results on Questions 1 and 2.

# Negative Exponent Patterns

Students see other ways to think about negative exponents.

## Mathematical Topics

- Understanding the definition of negative exponents in several ways
- Graphing $y = 2^x$ for positive, zero, and negative integer values of $x$

## *Outline of the Day*

### In Class

1. Select presenters for tomorrow's discussion of *POW 14: More from Lewis Carroll*
2. Discuss *Homework 7: Continuing the Pattern*
   - Bring out that the pattern of exponential expressions confirms yesterday's definition of exponentiation for negative exponents
3. Negative exponents and the additive law
   - Use the additive law of exponents as another way to confirm the definition of exponentiation for negative exponents
4. Extend the graph of $y = 2^x$
   - Use the definition of negative exponents to extend the graph to include negative values of $x$
5. Negative and zero exponents on calculators
   - Have students confirm that their calculators agree with the definition of exponentiation for zero and negative exponents

### At Home

*Homework 8: Negative Reflections*

## 1. POW Presentation Preparation

Presentations of *POW 14: More from Lewis Carroll* are scheduled for tomorrow. Choose three students to make POW presentations, and give them overhead transparencies and pens to take home to use in their preparations.

## 2. Discussion of *Homework 7: Continuing the Pattern*

Begin the discussion with the sequence of values in Question 1. You can have students explain the pattern, which might be articulated in various ways. For example, students might say, "Each value is half the one above it" or "Divide by 2 as you go down the list."

It will be helpful if you can get students to write the numerical values in several ways, as shown here—that is, as simplified fractions, as powers of $\frac{1}{2}$, and in the form $\frac{1}{2^B}$.

$$2^{-1} = \frac{1}{2}$$

$$2^{-2} = \frac{1}{4} = \left(\frac{1}{2}\right)^2 = \frac{1}{2^2}$$

$$2^{-3} = \frac{1}{8} = \left(\frac{1}{2}\right)^3 = \frac{1}{2^3}$$

$$2^{-4} = \frac{1}{16} = \left(\frac{1}{2}\right)^4 = \frac{1}{2^4}$$

***"How do these results relate to your work on 'Having Your Cake and Drinking Too'?"***

Ask students to relate the conclusions here to their work on negative exponents yesterday using Alice and the activity *Having Your Cake and Drinking Too*.

Use these examples to review and generalize the principle developed yesterday that we define $2^{-B}$ as $\frac{1}{2^B}$. Students should see that the pattern they just found for the powers of 2 is another reason it makes sense to define expressions with negative exponents the way we do. In fact, for many students, this is the most convincing and most easily remembered way to think about negative exponents.

Remind students, if necessary, that this was one of the ways that they explained the definition of zero as an exponent (see the section "The Exponential Pattern" from Day 3). *Note:* Another approach to defining negative exponents is dealt with in the next section, "Confirming the Definition Using the Additive Law of Exponents."

### • *Question 2*

Question 2 can be dealt with very briefly, as long as students see that similar patterns hold for any whole-number base. That is, students should see that in general, it seems to make sense to define $A^{-B}$ to be equal to $\frac{1}{A^B}$ .

### • *Question 3*

***"Does the general principle that $A^{-B}$ is defined as $\frac{1}{A^B}$ apply when A is equal to $\frac{1}{2}$?"***

In Question 3, students should see that they have simply reversed the pattern from Question 1. Ask whether the general principle that $A^{-B}$ is defined as $\frac{1}{A^B}$ is working here.

Help students to see that if this principle holds, then we are saying, for example, that $\left(\frac{1}{2}\right)^{-4}$ should be defined as

$$\frac{1}{\left(\frac{1}{2}\right)^{-4}}$$

The pattern suggests that $\left(\frac{1}{2}\right)^{-4}$ should be equal to 16 (which is $2^4$).

Ask students how to reconcile these two ideas. Specifically, this will require them to think about how to simplify a fraction like

$$\frac{1}{\left(\frac{1}{2}\right)^{-4}}$$

*Note:* A fraction like this, in which the numerator or denominator is itself a fraction, is called a **complex fraction.**

You may want to have students first look at the simpler case of

$$\frac{1}{\frac{1}{2}}$$

Here are two ways to think about simplifying this expression.

- Multiply both the numerator (which is 1) and the denominator (which is $\frac{1}{2}$) by 2. This gives the fraction

$$\frac{2 \cdot 1}{2 \cdot \frac{1}{2}}$$

  which simplifies to $\frac{2}{1}$, which equals 2. Bring out that this is the same process students always use in creating equivalent fractions, such as in expressing $\frac{1}{2}$ as $\frac{2}{4}$.

- Interpret the fraction as division, that is, as $1 \div \frac{1}{2}$, and use the "invert and multiply" rule to write this as $1 \cdot \frac{2}{1}$.

*Comment:* Both of these methods can be applied to any complex fraction of the form

$$\frac{\frac{a}{b}}{\frac{c}{d}}$$

To use the first method, multiply the numerator and the denominator by $\frac{d}{c}$. This can be thought of as a way of explaining the rather mysterious "invert and multiply" rule.

### • *Summing up*

Before using the additive law of exponents to confirm the definition, you may want to have a volunteer summarize the conclusions the class has reached about defining expressions with negative integer exponents.

Students may initially give you either a numerical example, such as $2^{-2} = \frac{1}{4}$, or a general principle, such as $A^{-B} = \frac{1}{A^B}$. But be sure to get the general principle stated clearly, perhaps in this way:

**An exponential expression with a negative exponent is defined by the equation**

$$A^{-B} = \frac{1}{A^B}$$

Post this principle for reference.

## 3. Confirming the Definition Using the Additive Law of Exponents

***"What is an example of the additive law of exponents that uses the expression $2^{-2}$?"***

Pick a particular expression with a negative exponent, such as 2-2, and have the class come up with an example of the additive law of exponents that uses this expression. Ask for an example in which the exponent on the right side comes out positive.

For example, a student might create this equation:

$$2^{-2} \cdot 2^5 = 2^{-2+5} = 2^3$$

Have students verify that the new definition is consistent with the additive law of exponents by substituting the values of each of the expressions—$\frac{1}{4}$ for $2^{-2}$, 32 for $2^5$, and 8 for $2^3$. With these values substituted, the equation becomes the true equation

$$\frac{1}{4} \cdot 32 = 8$$

Bring out that if $2^{-2}$ were replaced by any number other than $\frac{1}{4}$, the result would not be a true equation, so the only definition for $2^{-2}$ that works is $2^{-2} = \frac{1}{4}$.

Then have students try an example or two in which all the exponents are negative, such as

$$2^{-3} \cdot 2^{-2} = 2^{-3+(-2)} = 2^{-5}$$

They should see that substituting values based on the new definition gives the true equation

$$\frac{1}{8} \cdot \frac{1}{4} = \frac{1}{32}$$

A good special case to look at is one in which the exponents are opposites, such as $2^5 \cdot 2^{-5}$. Bring out that the exponents are "canceling out" to give a sum of 0, while the exponential expressions themselves also "cancel out" to give a product of 1.

- *More examples of cake and beverage*

Review the general phenomenon of positive and negative exponents in terms of the Alice metaphor. You can do this by presenting students with several combinations of cake and beverage—some with more cake, some with more beverage, some with equal amounts—and have them analyze the effect on Alice's height in two ways.

- Work with the two types of food sequentially (for example, first the cake, then the beverage) to see the effect on Alice's height.
- Combine the cake and beverage into a single amount of one or the other, using the intuitive idea that "equal amounts of cake and beverage cancel." (Students may see that cake and beverage are analogous to hot and cold cubes.)

Bring out that the two approaches give the same results. Help the class to verbalize the notion that in combining cake and beverage, they are treating the beverage as a kind of "negative cake." Therefore, the effect of $B$ ounces of beverage, which is to multiply Alice's height by $\frac{1}{2^B}$, should be the same as the effect of "$-B$ ounces" of cake. According to the general formula developed on Day 2, eating $-B$ ounces of cake should multiply Alice's height by $2^{-B}$. In other words, $\frac{1}{2^B}$ and $2^{-B}$ should be equal.

*Note:* This may seem somewhat repetitive. We are giving students several ways to see the same idea—that expressions with negative exponents are defined in terms of fractions—because it is a fairly abstract concept. Therefore, different students will assimilate different ways of thinking about it. The Day 12 activity *All Roads Lead to Rome* will review the various ways to think about extending the definition of exponential expressions beyond positive integer exponents.

## 4. Graphing $y = 2^x$

On Day 2, you probably posted a graph showing points from the equation $y = 2^x$ for positive integer values of $x$. As students worked with zero as an exponent, they saw that defining $2^0$ to be 1 seemed consistent with this graph. Now it's time to extend the graph to include negative integer values for $x$.

Back on Day 2, students speculated on what would happen if they extended the graph of $y = 2^x$ to include negative values of $x$ (see the subsection "Extending the graphs to the left"). Refer to the posted graph for positive integer values of $x$, and ask volunteers to add new points to that graph, first for $x$ with a value of 0 and then for negative integer values of $x$.

Although the scale of their earlier graph may make it hard to plot these points precisely, students should see that the general shape of the first quadrant portion of the graph is consistent with these new points. That is, as $x$ moves from larger to smaller positive values, the $y$-values are decreasing in a way that fits smoothly with new points at $(0, 1)$, $(-1, \frac{1}{2})$, $(-2, \frac{1}{4})$, and so on.

## 5. Negative and Zero Exponents on Calculators

Ask students to verify that their calculators (both graphing and scientific) give numerical results for zero and negative exponents that agree with the definitions developed so far in this unit.

Of course, for negative exponents, calculators will give results in decimal form. Students will need to check that these are equal to the common-fraction values that they have used in their definition. For example, if they try to evaluate $2^{-3}$, they will get 0.125, which they should recognize as being equal to $\frac{1}{8}$.

They should also confirm that graphing the equation $y = 2^x$ on the graphing calculator gives a result that matches the graph they have made by plotting individual points.

### • *Zero as a base*

***"What happens if you use 0 as the base with a negative exponent? Why?"***

This is a good place to bring up the question of what happens if 0 is used as the base with a negative exponent. Let students try this on their graphing calculators.

They should get an error message, and you can ask them why this happened. This should lead to a discussion of the issue of division by zero (if time permits) and the reason division by zero is undefined. (You may have had such a discussion on Day 5.)

At the same time, you can review the situation of $0^0$ (see the subsection "What about $0^0$?" on Day 6).

## *Homework 8: Negative Reflections*

This assignment gives students a chance to synthesize what they have learned so far about extending the concept of exponents.

# Homework 8 Negative Reflections

When you first learned about exponents, their use was defined in terms of repeated multiplication. For example, you defined $2^5$ as $2 \cdot 2 \cdot 2 \cdot 2 \cdot 2$.

With that repeated-multiplication definition, the exponent had to be a positive whole number. Now you have seen a way to make new definitions that allow zero and negative integers to be exponents.

1. Write a clear explanation summarizing what you have learned about defining expressions that have zero or a negative integer as an exponent. Then explain, using examples, why these definitions make sense. Give as many different reasons as you can, and indicate which explanation makes the most sense to you.

2. Show your explanation to an adult, and ask that person whether it made sense to him or her. Then write about the person's reaction.

All About Alice

# "Curiouser and Curiouser!"

***This page in the student book introduces Days 9 through 12.***

Alice thought it was "a curious feeling" when she began shrinking as a result of drinking her special beverage. You might have thought it was rather curious when you learned that zero and negative integers could be used as exponents.

"Curiouser and curiouser!" That's what Alice said when she learned about the special cake. Your adventures with exponents also get curiouser, as you go from integers to fractions in the next part of the unit.

***In "All Roads Lead to Rome," Adam Davenport, Dean Mertes, Tiffany Tomlin, and Joe Stebbins review the extension of exponentiation beyond positive integral exponents.***

# POW 14 Presentations

*Students present POW 14 and begin thinking about fractional exponents.*

## Mathematical Topics

- Working with logical inference
- Defining fractional exponents

## *Outline of the Day*

### In Class

1. Presentations of *POW 14: More from Lewis Carroll*
2. Discuss or simply collect *Homework 8: Negative Reflections*
3. *A Half Ounce of Cake*
   - Students begin to examine what happens if Alice eats a fraction of an ounce of cake
   - The activity will be discussed on Day 10

### At Home

*Homework 9: It's in the Graph*

*POW 15: A Logical Collection* (due Day 18)

## *Discuss With Your Colleagues*

### The Role of the Graph

**The graph of the exponential equation $y = 2^x$ is used in this unit as one of the tools for deciding how to extend the definition of exponentiation. (For example, see tonight's *Homework 9: It's in the Graph*.) How effective is this approach compared to the other ideas used?**

# 1. Presentations of *POW 14: More from Lewis Carroll*

One approach is to have the three students alternate presentations on the six problems. After each problem, you can let the other presenting students add any comments and then ask the rest of the class for comments.

• ***POW issues***

Here are some things to look for on individual problems.

1. Conclusion: "Senna is not nice."

   This is a straightforward example, so it is worth taking time to be sure that all students see why this conclusion is valid.

2. No new conclusion.

   You might point out that shillings are coins formerly used in Britain, but that this is not really relevant to the problem. Make sure all students see that they cannot conclude, "These coins are shillings."

3. Conclusion: "Some wild things are fat" (or "Some fat things are wild").

   Students may not see these as legitimate conclusions. If they decided that there was no possible new conclusion in this case, that's okay. It's a matter of opinion whether these conclusions are "new." But they should see that both of these conclusions must be true.

4. No new conclusion.

   Students may suggest as a conclusion "Some unprejudiced persons are liked." According to formal logic, this doesn't follow from statement b, although everyday usage suggests that if we say "some are . . ." then we also are saying "some are not . . ." This is worth discussing if it comes up. Point out that we often draw conclusions from things people say that are not necessarily implied by what they say.

5. Main conclusion: "Babies cannot manage a crocodile."

   There are other, subsidiary conclusions that use only two of the three statements, such as:

   - "Babies are despised." (from a and c)
   - "Illogical persons cannot manage a crocodile." (from b and c)

   You can discuss how the main conclusion can be drawn by combining one of the subsidiary statements with the remaining one of the original statements.

6. Main conclusion: "No bird in this aviary lives on mince pies." (This conclusion uses all four statements in the problem.)

   In this problem there are even more subsidiary conclusions:

   - "All of my birds are ostriches." (from a and d)
   - "No birds in this aviary are less than 9 feet high." (from b and d)
   - "No birds that are 9 feet high live on mince pies." (from a and c)

Try not to get caught up in technicalities such as whether ostriches are *exactly* 9 feet high or *at least* 9 feet high. Also, help students to realize that none of the statements in Question 6 guarantees that there are any birds in the aviary or that "I" have any birds. In general, a statement like "All $x$'s are $y$" doesn't mean that there are any $x$'s.

- *Part II: Creating Examples*

When the specific problems from the POW have been discussed, you can ask the presenters (or perhaps volunteers) to each give one of the examples they made up for Part II of the POW. Then let the class work on these.

## 2. Discussion of *Homework 8: Negative Reflections*

This is a good assignment for you to use to assess students' understanding of the ideas. (You will probably benefit from reading at least a selection of students' explanations, even if you choose not to grade the assignment.) Students' explanations in Question 1 in particular should give you a good idea of how well they have understood the principles involved in extending the definition of exponentiation.

You may want to briefly discuss how adults reacted to the ideas.

## 3. *A Half Ounce of Cake*

The next activity, *A Half Ounce of Cake,* continues the process of extending the meaning of exponentiation. In this activity, students will begin to consider fractional exponents.

As students begin work on *A Half Ounce of Cake,* you may want to emphasize that they should think about what Alice's height is *multiplied by* if she eats half an ounce of cake.

- *Some hints for groups*

You will probably find groups whose members think that eating half an ounce of cake multiplies Alice's height by 1.5. You might even try to argue students into this mistake by saying something like

> "Eating a whole ounce doubles Alice's height, which is a 100 percent increase. So eating half an ounce should increase her height by 50 percent, right?"

You can have students start with a specific height for Alice and see what would happen to her height if it were increased twice each time by

50 percent. Students will probably understand the situation better once they see that two 50 percent increases of Alice's height will more than double her height. You can then ask what a single 50 percent increase multiplies Alice's height by.

You might also ask students to create an example of the additive law of exponents that shows Alice eating half an ounce and then another half, as suggested in the hint for Question 1. Perhaps someone will see that this situation can be represented by the equation

$$2^{1/2} \cdot 2^{1/2} = 2^1$$

You can then suggest that they replace each instance of $2^{1/2}$ with a box and replace $2^1$ with 2, as below, and ask what number should go in each box (the same number in both) to fit this equation.

As needed, use some combination of these hints to help students see that they are looking for a number that, multiplied by itself, gives a result of 2.

$$\square \cdot \square = 2$$

*Note:* Students may not identify the number being described as $\sqrt{2}$, and that's fine for now.

Encourage students who are having trouble finding a number that works to guess and check with the help of a calculator. But do not tell them to enter the expression $2^{1/2}$ directly into their calculators.

This activity will be discussed on Day 10. You may want to give overhead transparencies and pens to the first groups that finish, so they can prepare a presentation of their findings for tomorrow.

This activity deals only with pieces of cake that are *unit fractions*—fractions that have a numerator of 1 and a denominator that is a positive integer. More general fractional exponents will be part of *Homework 10: Stranger Pieces of Cake.*

## *Homework 9: It's in the Graph*

In tonight's homework, students will approach the problem of defining $2^{1/2}$ in terms of the graph of the equation $y = 2^x$. They can work on this assignment whether or not they have made significant progress on *A Half Ounce of Cake.*

# POW 15: A Logical Collection

The group of problems in this new POW continues the theme of logical reasoning begun in *POW 14: More from Lewis Carroll*. This POW is scheduled for discussion on Day 18.

***Diane Wong, Wendy Chicas, Darlene Cardenas, Eduardo Perez, Phong La, Roxana Martinez, and Marcela Peniche are working with graphing calculators to explore the meaning of fractional exponents.***

# A Half Ounce of Cake

One day, as Alice was wandering through Wonderland, she stumbled across a silver plate with a small piece of cake on it. Alice picked up the cake and could tell by the size and feel of it that it weighed exactly half an ounce. She also could tell from the aroma and texture that this was base 2 cake.

1. We all know that eating an ounce of this cake will double Alice's height. But what will eating half an ounce multiply her height by? (*Hint:* Keep in mind that eating half an ounce of cake and then eating another half ounce should have the same effect as eating one ounce of cake.)
2. Investigate what Alice's height is multiplied by if she eats other fractional pieces of cake, such as a third of an ounce or a fifth of an ounce.

# Homework 9 It's in the Graph

What's $2^{1/2}$?

Maybe you know and maybe you don't. If you don't know, a graph could help you find out. If you do know, a graph will give you another way of thinking about that number.

In *Homework 1: Graphing Alice,* you made a graph showing what Alice's height is multiplied by if she eats various amounts of cake. As you have seen, that graph showed points that fit the equation $y = 2^x$.

In that graph, you considered only positive integers for $x$. You now know how to interpret the expression $2^x$ when $x$ is any integer.

1. a. Make an In-Out table for the equation $y = 2^x$ using the values -2, -1, 0, 1, and 2 for $x$. Then plot the points from your table and connect them with a smooth curve.

   b. Use your graph from part a to estimate the value of $2^{1/2}$.

*Continued on next page*

The curve you drew in Question 1b went through the specific points (0, 1) and (1, 2). Question 2 deals with the graph of the equation of the *line* through these two points.

2. a. Draw the graph of the equation $y = x + 1$ on the same axes you used for Question 1.

   b. Compare the two graphs. What does this comparison tell you about the value of $2^{1/2}$?

3. Parts a, b, and c below are similar to the process you used in Question 1.

   a. Make an In-Out table for the equation $y = 3^x$ using the values −2, −1, 0, 1, and 2 for $x$. Then plot the points, connect them with a smooth curve, and use your graph to estimate the value of $3^{1/2}$.

   b. Use a similar process to estimate the value of $9^{1/2}$ by making a table for the equation $y = 9^x$, plotting and connecting the points, and estimating.

   c. Use a similar process to estimate the value of $\left(\frac{1}{2}\right)^{1/2}$, using the equation $y = \left(\frac{1}{2}\right)^x$.

math goals: logical reasoning/deductive
math developed:





# POW 15 A Logical Collection

This POW is somewhat different from most in that it contains three separate problems. What these problems have in common is that they involve logical reasoning to figure out who is telling the truth.

Your write-up for each problem should explain how you solved it and how you can prove that your answers are correct.

## Part I: The Missing Mascot

The mascot of Goldenrod High is a stuffed ostrich, and it sits outside the main office. Just before the big game, the ostrich disappeared, and three students from arch-rival Greenview High are being questioned.

Each of the suspected students has made some statements.

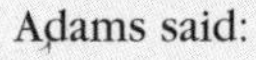

Adams said:

- "I didn't do it."
- "Benitez was hanging out near Goldenrod that day."

Benitez said:

- "I didn't do it."
- "I've never been inside Goldenrod."
- "Besides, I was out of town all that week."

Clark said:

- "I didn't do it."
- "I saw Adams and Benitez near Goldenrod that day."
- "One of them did it."

Assume that two of these students are innocent and are telling the truth, but that the third student is guilty and may be lying. Who did it? Prove your answer.

*Continued on next page*



Adam NO    Benitez ~~Hang Out~~ NO    Clark

| Adams | Benitez | Clark |
|---|---|---|

# Part II: What Did He Say?

You have found a strange place where some people always tell the truth and the rest always lie. Unfortunately, there's no way to tell from looking at them which is which.

You find yourself sitting with three of these people and decide to try to determine who belongs to which category. For simplicity, we'll refer to the three people as A, B, and C.

Here's the conversation.

> You say to A: "Are you a truth-teller or a liar?"
>
> A answers your question, but a squawking bird prevents you from hearing the answer.
>
> B says: "A says he's a truth-teller."
>
> C says: "B is lying."

What can you figure out from this conversation? What can't you figure out? Prove your answers.

# Part III: The Turner Triplets

The Turner triplets have a policy that whenever anyone asks them a question, two of them tell the truth and the other one lies. You have just asked them all which one was born first.

Here are their answers.

> Virna: "I am not the oldest."
>
> Werner: "Virna was born first."
>
> Myrna: "Werner is the oldest."

Who was born first? Prove your answer.

# DAY 10 Fractional Pieces of Cake

*Students use the Alice metaphor to define expressions with fractional exponents.*

## Mathematical Topics

- Giving meaning to the use of unit fractions as exponents
- Developing the language and notation of roots
- Using the graphs of functions like $y = 2^x$ for whole numbers to suggest the value of $2^{1/2}$ and similar expressions

## *Outline of the Day*

### In Class

1. Discuss *A Half Ounce of Cake* (from Day 9)
   - Use the Alice metaphor to define specific expressions of the form $2^{1/n}$
2. Using the language and notation of roots
   - Introduce the terminology and notation
   - Emphasize that the notation of roots can be used to represent the exact value
3. Define expressions with exponents that are unit fractions
   - Generalize the results from *A Half Ounce of Cake*
   - Confirm that calculators give results that are consistent with the definitions
   - Clarify the connection between roots and fractional exponents
4. Discuss *Homework 9: It's in the Graph*
   - Confirm that the definitions for fractional exponents are consistent with the estimates from the graph

### At Home

*Homework 10: Stranger Pieces of Cake*

*Note:* Discussion of last night's homework follows the discussion of yesterday's activity, *A Half Ounce of Cake*. (The discussion of *A Half Ounce of Cake* is essential for tonight's homework, while the discussion of last night's homework is not.)

## Discuss With Your Colleagues

### Roots or Fractional Exponents?

**In the discussion of *A Half Ounce of Cake,* students need to recognize that there are two ways to express certain numbers—as roots and with fractional exponents. Is this confusing? Why are both necessary? Has the balance between the two forms changed because of calculators? Has the radical sign become obsolete?**

## 1. Discussion of *A Half Ounce of Cake*

If a group has prepared a presentation on Question 1, let the spade card student make that presentation. (If not, you can ask for a volunteer.)

The presentation should bring out clearly that Question 1 calls for a number whose square is 2. If necessary, use some of the hints suggested in yesterday's introduction to the activity to bring this out.

Ask for explanations from other groups as well, trying to get as many different explanations as possible.

- *Using an exponent of $\frac{1}{2}$*

If necessary, remind the class of the general formula—that eating $C$ ounces of cake multiplies Alice's height by $2^C$—and ask how that fact applies to this situation. Be sure students see that the answer to Question 1 tells them how they should define $2^{1/2}$.

- *Using the additive law of exponents*

If no one suggests use of the additive law of exponents, ask for an explanation defining $2^{1/2}$ based on that principle (see yesterday's introduction for details). Although students may have seen that eating half an ounce of cake multiplies Alice's height by about 1.4, they may not make a connection between this number and the use of a fractional exponent.

- *Square root of 2*

***"What do you call the number whose square is 2?"***

Ask what the number whose square is 2 is called. Students will probably recall the term *square root,* and you should review the notation $\sqrt{2}$ if needed. Students should be able to find a good estimate for $\sqrt{2}$ both by using the square-root key on a calculator and by guess-and-check. Thus, students should see that $2^{1/2}$ equals $\sqrt{2}$.

### • *Question 2*

Once students have grasped that for half an ounce of cake, they need a number whose square is 2, they should easily extend the idea to other fractional pieces of cake. Thus, they should see, for example, that if Alice eats a piece of cake that weighs a third of an ounce, her height will be multiplied by the number whose *third* power is 2. They should use guess-and-check on their calculators to find a solution to the equation $x^3 = 2$.

## 2. The Language and Notation of Roots

This will be many students' first exposure to the general terminology and notation of roots, so don't make any assumptions here about their familiarity with this topic.

***"If the solution to $x^2 = 2$ is called the square root of 2, what would you call the solution to $x^3 = 2$?"***

You can point out that the solution to the equation $x^2 = 2$ is called the *square root of 2* and ask students what they think the solution to the equation $x^3 = 2$ should be called. If they suggest "third root of 2" (which is likely), point out that the expression $x^3$ itself is usually read as "$x$ cubed," not as "$x$ to the third power," so the solution to $x^3 = 2$ is generally called the **cube root of $x$** (and not the *third* root of $x$). Also, introduce the notation $\sqrt[3]{2}$ for this number. (You may want to emphasize that this terminology and notation is standard in mathematics.)

### • *Other roots*

***"What do you think the notation $\sqrt[5]{2}$ represents?"***

Follow up the introduction of the notation $\sqrt[3]{2}$ by asking what the notation $\sqrt[5]{2}$ represents. Students should recognize that this is the solution to the equation $x^5 = 2$. Introduce the phrase *fifth root of 2* for this number.

Point out that we could write $\sqrt[2]{2}$ for the square root of 2, but we don't. Also mention that the symbol $\sqrt{\ }$ is called the **radical sign.** (The word *radical* comes from a Latin word root that actually means "root.")

### • *$\sqrt{2}$ is exact*

No doubt, some students will wonder why 1.41 is not sufficient for $\sqrt{2}$. If the class does not raise this issue, you might want to do so yourself.

Tell the students that there is no decimal they can write whose square is exactly 2, so if they want to represent the number exactly, they need to use the symbol $\sqrt{2}$. (The issue of approximating and the effect of rounding were discussed in the unit *Do Bees Build It Best?*—especially *Homework 19: Falling Bridges*—but a little reminder of the consequences of rounding will not hurt.)

*Note:* Students will reexamine the use of a symbol to represent an exact value when they study $\pi$ in the Year 3 unit *Orchard Hideout.*

# 3. Defining Fractional Exponents

As discussed earlier, students may see that eating half an ounce of cake multiplies Alice's height by $\sqrt{2}$ but not see an immediate connection to the idea of fractional exponents. Although the connection may have come up for half an ounce, students may not have extended it to other fractions, so further discussion is in order.

***"What do these problems tell us about fractional exponents?"***

After completing the discussion of *A Half Ounce of Cake,* return to the issue of extending the meaning of exponents. You can begin with a general question, such as, "What do these problems tell us about fractional exponents?"

If necessary, go back to the basics and review the general principle about Alice—that eating $C$ ounces of cake multiplies her height by $2^C$.

You can follow this up by asking what happens if Alice eats half an ounce of cake. Help students to see that according to the general principle, Alice's height is multiplied by $2^{1/2}$, but their work in the activity showed that her height should be multiplied by $\sqrt{2}$.

You may need to remind students that as with negative and zero exponents, the "repeated multiplication" definition doesn't work for fractional exponents, and so we need to *define* the expression $2^{1/2}$ by some other method. Students should see that their work suggests that it makes sense to define $2^{1/2}$ as $\sqrt{2}$ and, similarly, $2^{1/3}$ as $\sqrt[3]{2}$ and $2^{1/5}$ as $\sqrt[5]{2}$.

You will probably want to get a summary of these ideas, as well as perhaps post a general principle along the lines of

$$A^{1/n} = \sqrt[n]{A}$$

Have students check that their calculators agree with defining $2^{1/2}$ as $\sqrt{2}$. That is, they should verify that the calculator gives the same answer for both. (There is more discussion on the use of calculators later today.)

*Note:* With many calculators, it's necessary to put parentheses around a fraction used as an exponent. For example, if the calculator uses the symbol ^ for exponentiation (writing 2 ^ 5 for $2^5$), it will probably interpret the expression 2 ^ 1/2 as $(2^1) \div 2$, which equals 1. The sure way to get the value of $2^{1/2}$ is to enter 2 ^ (1/2).

## • *Optional: A context for cubes and cube roots*

***"Why is the expression $2^3$ read 'two cubed'?"***

You may want to take a brief detour to bring out a context in which cubes and cube roots are important. You can begin by asking the class why the expression $2^3$ is read "two cubed" (rather than as "two to the third power").

If necessary, ask if anyone can think of a meaning for "cube" other than raising a number to the third power. This should elicit mention of the geometric meaning—that a cube is a solid figure with perpendicular sides of equal length.

Ask why this same word is used for third powers. Students should recall enough about volume from *Do Bees Build It Best?* to explain that the volume of a cube is the cube of the length of its side. You might do a few simple examples, such as asking what the volume is for a cube with sides of length 5.

***"How would you find the length of the side of a cube if you knew that its volume was, say, 40 cubic inches?"***

Then ask how one would find the length of a side of a cube if one knew the volume. You may want to use a numerical example. Students will see that the cube root of the volume gives the desired length.

- *Roots and fractional exponents on calculators*

Have students explore, on both their graphing calculators and their scientific calculators, how to find the numerical value of roots and expressions using exponents that are unit fractions.

Some scientific calculators have a $\sqrt[x]{y}$ key (often as a "second function" with the $y^x$ key). On many calculators, to use the $\sqrt[x]{y}$ key, you enter the $y$-value, then use the $\sqrt[x]{y}$ key, and then enter the $x$-value. Thus, for example, a key sequence like

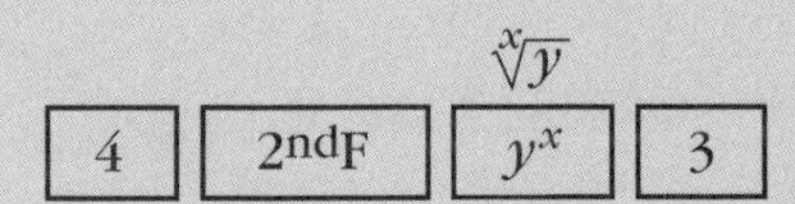


might be used to represent $\sqrt[3]{4}$. (On some calculators, you enter $x$ first.)

Some calculators do not have such a key (many graphing calculators do not), and with these calculators, the only way to find roots other than square roots is by using fractional exponents.

Calculators can be used as a format for helping students make the connection between roots and fractional exponents. That is, they should understand that the expression $a^{1/n}$ means the same thing as $\sqrt[n]{a}$.

## 4. Discussion of *Homework 9: It's in the Graph*

The discussion of last night's *Homework 9: It's in the Graph* can be used to confirm the reasonableness of the definition that has been developed for an exponent of $\frac{1}{2}$. Students should see that the estimates provided by the graphical analysis on their homework are consistent with this definition.

## • *Questions 1 and 2*

We suggest that you go directly to the comparison of graphs in Question 2, because that enables you to bring out graphically that $2^{1/2}$ should be less than 1.5.

Ask for a volunteer to present Question 2. The presenter should note that the graph of the equation $y = x + 1$ goes through the point (0.5, 1.5). Students have already seen that the graph of the equation $y = 2^x$ is curved, and when $x$ is equal to 0.5, this graph is below the straight line through (0, 1) and (1, 2). The combined graph here illustrates this idea. (A large version of this diagram for making a transparency is included in Appendix B.)

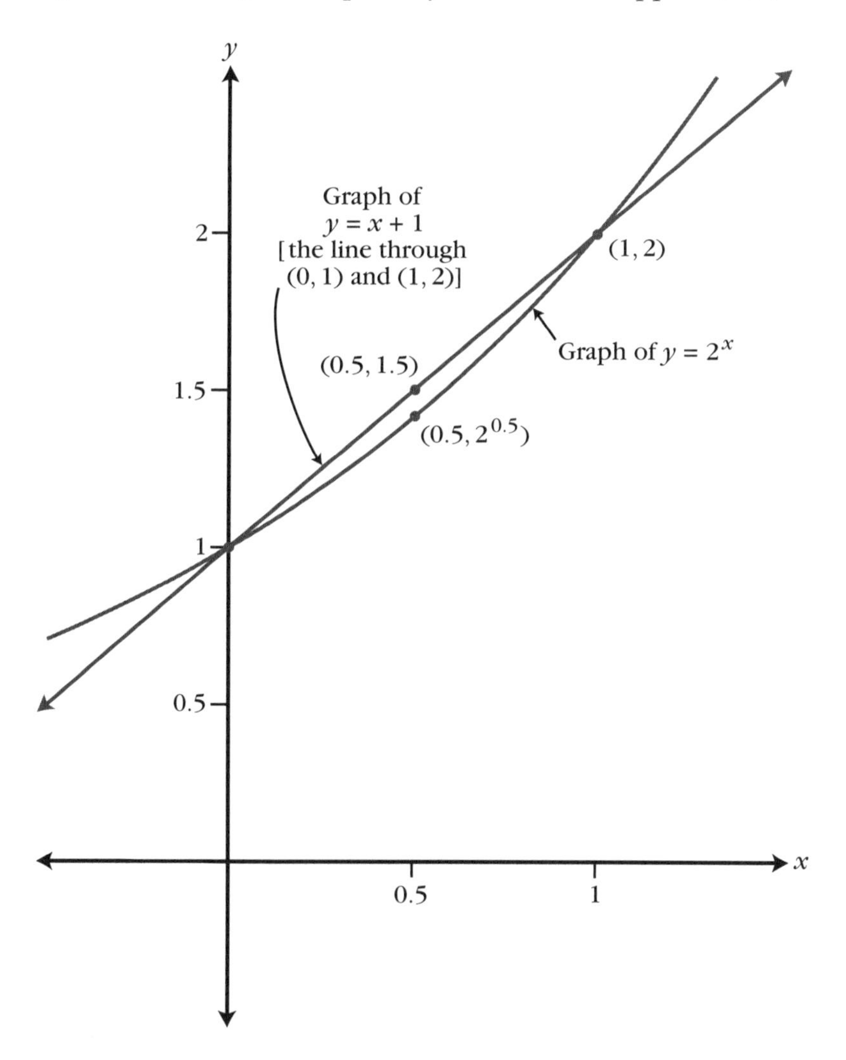


Students can also use a graphing calculator to graph the function $y = 2^x$, and then use the trace feature to get another estimate for $2^{0.5}$. That is, they should find the $y$-coordinate of the point on this graph for which $x$ equals 0.5.

This procedure should give them a more precise value for $2^{0.5}$ than they can get from a hand-made graph. Use of the zoom feature will give them as much precision as they want. Make sure students realize that the $y$-coordinate has the numerical value of $\sqrt{2}$ and that their reading is an approximation of this value.

- *Question 3*

There is no pressing need to go over Question 3, but if time allows, here are some ways to make use of students' work on this.

- Use the question to review the general graphs of other exponential functions. In particular, bring out that they all go through (0, 1).
- See that the graph in Question 3b (the graph of the equation $y = 9^x$) seems to confirm that $9^{1/2} = 3$.
- Discuss the difference between the graph in Question 3c and the other examples.

*Note:* You may want to have students record their estimates for $\left(\frac{1}{2}\right)^{1/2}$ to compare with the value of $2^{-1/2}$ that will be obtained tomorrow.

## Homework 10: Stranger Pieces of Cake

This homework follows up on the classwork to deal with nonunit fractions used as exponents.

How does this effect Alice's height
Describe





# Homework 10 Stranger Pieces of Cake

In the activity *A Half Ounce of Cake,* you saw how to use Alice's situation to make sense of certain fractional exponents, such as $\frac{1}{2}$ and $\frac{1}{3}$, where the numerator of the fraction is 1. (These are called **unit fractions.**) But what about fractional exponents in general?

In this assignment, you will investigate the effect of fractional pieces of cake where the fraction's numerator is not 1.

1. Start with a piece of base 2 cake that weighs $\frac{3}{5}$ of an ounce. What effect should eating this have on Alice's height? Explain your answer.
2. Use your work on Question 1 to give a general way of defining $2^{p/q}$ for any fraction $\frac{p}{q}$. Explain your ideas.

$2^{\frac{3}{5}}$

$\sqrt[5]{2^3}$

$\sqrt[5]{2} \cdot \sqrt[5]{2} \cdot \sqrt[5]{2}$

$(2^3)^{\frac{1}{5}}$

$(2^{\frac{1}{5}})^3$

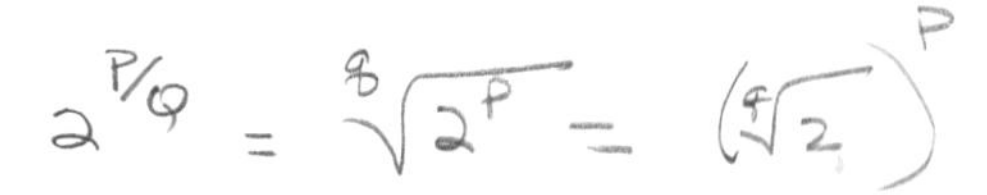

$2^{P/Q} = \sqrt[Q]{2^P} = (\sqrt[Q]{2})^P$

# Day 11 Strange Cake

Students extend the definition of exponentiation from unit fractions to arbitrary fractions.

## Mathematical Topics

- Working with general fractional exponents, including negative fractions
- Developing the general exponential function

## Outline of the Day

### In Class

1. Form new random groups
2. Discuss *Homework 10: Stranger Pieces of Cake*
   - Develop the general definition for fractional exponents
3. Define exponentiation for negative fractions
4. Define the general exponential function
   - Complete the graph of the function $y = 2^x$
   - Generalize to arbitrary positive bases

### At Home

*Homework 11: Confusion Reigns*

## 1. Forming New Groups

This is an excellent time to place the students in new random groups. Follow the procedure described in the IMP *Teaching Handbook,* and record the groups and the suit for each student.

## 2. Discussion of *Homework 10: Stranger Pieces of Cake*

You can expect students to have more difficulty understanding how to interpret an expression like $2^{3/5}$ than they had for expressions in which the exponent was a unit fraction. You can ask for volunteers to explain their work on the homework questions, and let other students add further ideas.

Students typically approach this by saying that eating a $\frac{3}{5}$-ounce piece of cake is the same as eating three separate $\frac{1}{5}$-ounce pieces. Because each $\frac{1}{5}$-ounce piece of cake multiplies Alice's height by $\sqrt[5]{2}$, eating three such pieces will multiply Alice's height by $\left(\sqrt[5]{2}\right)^3$. Thus, it makes sense to define $2^{3/5}$ as $\left(\sqrt[5]{2}\right)^3$.

- ***Another approach***

An alternate approach to evaluating $2^{3/5}$ is to imagine Alice eating five pieces of cake, each weighing $\frac{3}{5}$ of an ounce. This would be a total of 3 ounces of cake, so it would multiply Alice's height by $2^3$ or 8. Because five of these $\frac{3}{5}$-ounce pieces together multiply Alice's height by 8, one such piece would multiply her height by $\sqrt[5]{8}$.

Thus, the first approach sees $2^{3/5}$ as $\left(\sqrt[5]{2}\right)^3$, and the second approach sees $2^{3/5}$ as $\sqrt[5]{2^3}$. Students can verify that these are equal.

One way to prove that $\left(\sqrt[5]{2}\right)^3$ is the same as $\sqrt[5]{2^3}$, based on general laws of exponents, is to use the sequence of equalities

$$\left[\left(\sqrt[5]{2}\right)^3\right]^5 = \left(\sqrt[5]{2}\right)^{15} = \left[\left(\sqrt[5]{2}\right)^5\right]^3 = 2^3$$

which shows that $\left(\sqrt[5]{2}\right)^3$ is the fifth root of $2^3$.

- ***Question 2: Defining $2^{p/q}$***

If students define $2^{3/5}$ as $\left(\sqrt[5]{2}\right)^3$, they will probably not have much trouble generalizing this to see that eating a piece of cake weighing $\frac{p}{q}$ ounces is like eating $p$ pieces that each weigh $\frac{1}{q}$ ounces.

Because each $\frac{1}{q}$-ounce piece multiplies Alice's height by $\sqrt[q]{2}$, $p$ such pieces should multiply her height by $\left(\sqrt[q]{2}\right)^p$. Therefore, it makes sense to define $2^{p/q}$ as $\left(\sqrt[q]{2}\right)^p$.

- ***Optional: A "consistency test" for equivalent fractions***

This definition poses an interesting "consistency test" as to whether equivalent fractions give the same results.

For example, students know that $\frac{6}{10}$ equals $\frac{3}{5}$. You can ask them whether $\left(\sqrt[10]{2}\right)^6$ is equal to $\left(\sqrt[5]{2}\right)^3$. Using fractional exponents makes this appear "obvious," but working with powers of roots shows that there is some thinking needed. (As a hint, suggest that students raise both expressions to the tenth power and then apply some laws of exponents to get $2^6$ for each.)

## 3. Defining Negative Fractional Exponents

***"How should we define $2^{-1/2}$?"***

One more step will extend the definition of exponentiation to include all rational numbers as exponents. To begin, ask if anyone has an idea how one should define $2^{-1/2}$. If needed, suggest that there might be a way to use Alice's beverage for assistance. That is, $2^{-1/2}$ should be the amount Alice's height is multiplied by if she drinks half an ounce of the beverage.

Help students to see that, because a whole ounce of beverage multiplies Alice's height by $\frac{1}{2}$, half an ounce of beverage should multiply her height by $\sqrt{\frac{1}{2}}$.

***"Does this definition fit the earlier principle that $A^{-B} = \frac{1}{A^B}$?"***

Ask if this definition fits the earlier principle

$$A^{-B} = \frac{1}{A^B}$$

If necessary, help students see that

- one approach defines $2^{-1/2}$ as $\sqrt{\frac{1}{2}}$
- the other approach defines $2^{-1/2}$ as $\frac{1}{2^{1/2}}$

Work with students to see that

$$\sqrt{\frac{1}{2}} = \frac{1}{2^{1/2}}$$

*Suggestion:* In *Homework 18: Simply Square Roots* in *Do Bees Build It Best?* students worked with the general principle

$$\sqrt{\frac{a}{b}} = \frac{\sqrt{a}}{\sqrt{b}}$$

which shows that

$$\sqrt{\frac{1}{2}} = \frac{1}{\sqrt{2}}$$

But the denominator $\sqrt{2}$ is equal to $2^{1/2}$, so we get

$$\sqrt{\frac{1}{2}} = \frac{1}{2^{1/2}}$$

### • *Comparison with $\left(\frac{1}{2}\right)^{1/2}$*

If students recorded their estimates of $\left(\frac{1}{2}\right)^{1/2}$ when you discussed Question 3c of *Homework 9: It's in the Graph*, have them compare those estimates to the value of $\sqrt{\frac{1}{2}}$. They should see that the results are approximately the same. You can ask them to explain why $\left(\frac{1}{2}\right)^{1/2}$ and $\sqrt{\frac{1}{2}}$ should be equal.

# 4. The General Exponential Function

One important idea that should come out of this discussion is that the function $y = 2^x$ makes sense for *any* number $x$.

> At this stage, students may have at best only a hazy notion that there are such things as irrational numbers, so you won't be able to discuss the "complete" exponential function in a formal sense. But students should see that they have defined it for all rational exponents (for a positive base), and that should persuade them that they can make sense of any exponential expression with a positive base.

You can bring out this point by asking how an expression like $2^{0.562}$ could be interpreted in terms of the Alice situation. Students should be able to articulate that this number is what Alice's height would be multiplied by if she ate 0.562 ounces of cake. They also should be able to articulate that theoretically they could find this number by thinking of this as 562 pieces, each weighing $\frac{1}{1000}$ of an ounce, and that each of those pieces would multiply Alice's height by $\sqrt[1000]{2}$, so that

$$2^{0.562} = \left(\sqrt[1000]{2}\right)^{562}$$

Similarly, $2^{-0.562}$ represents the factor by which Alice's height is multiplied if she drinks 0.562 ounces of beverage.

***"Does the expression $2^x$ make sense for all values of $x$?"***

After looking at such examples, ask explicitly if the expression $2^x$ makes sense for all values of $x$. Students should see that it at least makes sense when $x$ is a rational number. (If they raise questions about irrational exponents, you can tell them that the definition can be extended using repeated approximations and the concept of a *limit*.)

- *The complete graph*

This is a good occasion to look once again at the graph of $y = 2^x$ as a whole. Have students graph this function on graphing calculators, and check (using zoom and trace) to see that the coordinates of points on the graph are consistent with all the definitions that they have formulated in extending the operation of exponentiation to include zero, negative, and fractional exponents.

- *The general base and exponent*

Finally, bring out that the work that has just been done with base 2 could be done with any positive base. Although students will probably be less comfortable with bases between 0 and 1 than with bases greater than 1, they should be able to see that the expression $b^x$ makes sense for any value of $x$, provided that $b$ is a positive number.

You might discuss a "random-looking" example such as $0.416^{-6.78}$ to illustrate how such a general definition would work. For instance, students can describe this as the factor by which Alice's height is multiplied if she drinks 6.78 ounces of base 0.416 beverage, and they should see that this number is equal to

$$\frac{1}{\left(\sqrt[100]{0.416}\right)^{678}}$$

## *Homework 11: Confusion Reigns*

This homework reviews ideas developed in *Homework 5: In Search of the Law*. It also seeks to discourage students from simply memorizing rules about exponents by showing them that there are lots of "potential rules" but that only some of them really work.

***Erica Dommer and Shannon Campbell estimate values of $2^{p/q}$ from their graph of $y = 2^x$.***

# Homework 11 Confusion Reigns

The students at Bayside High School are learning some fancy stuff about exponents, and there seems to be some confusion. They are trying to come up with some other generalizations besides the additive law of exponents.

1. Bill says,

   "$3^4 + 3^5 = 3^9$, because $4 + 5 = 9$."

   Jill says,

   "$3^4 + 3^5 = 6^9$, because $4 + 5 = 9$ and $3 + 3 = 6$."

   Do either of them know what's going on? Don't simply give yes or no answers. Bill and Jill need some good explanations if they are going to understand how to work with exponents.

*Continued on next page*

2. Randy, Sandy, and Dandy each say that they have a way to multiply expressions with the same exponent.

   Randy says,

   "$2^3 \cdot 5^3 = 10^6$, because $2 \cdot 5 = 10$ and $3 + 3 = 6$."

   Sandy says,

   "$2^3 \cdot 5^3 = 10^9$, because $2 \cdot 5 = 10$ and $3 \cdot 3 = 9$."

   Dandy says,

   "$2^3 \cdot 5^3 = 10^3$, because $2 \cdot 5 = 10$ and the exponent doesn't change."

   Again, do any of them know what's going on? And, again, don't simply give yes or no answers. Try to come up with a particular rule for multiplying expressions with exponents when the exponents are the same, and give good explanations for your answers.

3. Fran, Jan, and Stan want to raise exponential expressions to powers.

   Fran says,

   "$(7^2)^3 = 7^5$, because $2 + 3 = 5$."

   Jan says,

   "$(7^2)^3 = 7^6$, because $2 \cdot 3 = 6$."

   Stan says,

   "$(7^2)^3 = 7^8$, because $2^3 = 8$."

   Once again, who's right and who's wrong? And, once again, don't simply give yes or no answers. Try to come up with a rule for raising exponential expressions to powers, and give a good explanation for your answer.

# Reflecting on Exponents

*Students begin to synthesize their ideas about exponents.*

## Mathematical Topics

- Developing rules and "nonrules" for working with exponents
- Explaining the definitions of exponential expressions when the exponents are not natural numbers

## Outline of the Day

### In Class

1. Discuss *Homework 11: Confusion Reigns*
   - Have students use expressions with repeated multiplication to explain the general principles
2. *All Roads Lead to Rome*
   - Students use several approaches to explain the extended definition of exponentiation
   - The activity will be discussed on Day 13

### At Home

*Homework 12: Measuring Meals for Alice*

## 1. Discussion of *Homework 11: Confusion Reigns*

You may want to let students spend some time in groups debating answers to the homework. They will be able to verify which equations are numerically correct by doing the arithmetic, so the focus of the discussion should be on explanations and on finding general rules. Although the principles needed for Questions 2 and 3 were discussed earlier (see *Homework 5: In Search of the Law* and the activity *Many Meals for Alice* from Day 5), this is a good opportunity for students to review the ideas.

You can ask the club card members of different groups to report. The discussion below summarizes the key mathematical ideas.

- *Question 1*

There are no simple rules for adding numbers with exponents, whether the bases are the same or different. This "nonrule" may be worth remembering.

- *Question 2*

The general principle for multiplying when the exponents are the same (whether the bases are different or not) is

$$A^B \cdot C^B = (A \cdot C)^B$$

which is in line with Dandy's idea.

Have a student explain in detail how the specifics of Dandy's example work. As a hint, ask how to write $2^3 \cdot 5^3$ using repeated multiplication. As discussed in connection with *Homework 5: In Search of the Law,* students should be able to write this expression as a product of individual factors, as

$$2 \cdot 2 \cdot 2 \cdot 5 \cdot 5 \cdot 5$$

and then rearrange the factors in pairs, as

$$(2 \cdot 5) \cdot (2 \cdot 5) \cdot (2 \cdot 5)$$

to show that this is equal to $10^3$.

- *Question 3*

You can help students relate this to their work on *Many Meals for Alice* (Day 5). They should see that Jan has the right idea by finding a general rule like

$$\left(A^B\right)^C = A^{BC}$$

As with Question 2, have students show the details for a numerical example in terms of repeated multiplication. For instance, in terms of the example in Question 3, they should see that $\left(7^2\right)^3$ means $7^2 \cdot 7^2 \cdot 7^2$ and that each factor of $7^2$ is equal to $7 \cdot 7$. Thus

$$\left(7^2\right)^3 = 7^2 \cdot 7^2 \cdot 7^2 = (7 \cdot 7) \cdot (7 \cdot 7) \cdot (7 \cdot 7)$$

The "outside exponent" of 3 means that there are three sets of 7's, and the "inside exponent" of 2 means that there are two 7's in each set. Students should be able to explain that three sets of 7's with two 7's in each set gives a total of six 7's, because $3 \cdot 2$ equals 6. And because the six 7's are multiplied together, the result is equal to $7^6$.

- ***What's important?***

So what's important here? It would be nice if students used

$$A^B \cdot C^B = (A \cdot C)^B$$

or

$$\left(A^B\right)^C = A^{BC}$$

when they came across situations like these. What's more important is the recognition that such laws of exponents eventually boil down to understanding what exponents are and that the laws can be "re-created" if students take the time to write out the exponential expressions using repeated multiplication.

## 2. *All Roads Lead to Rome*

Students have been using several approaches to gain an understanding of the extension of exponentiation beyond positive integer exponents. *All Roads Lead to Rome* gives them a chance to review and reflect on this variety of perspectives.

This activity will be included in students' portfolios for this unit and will be discussed on Day 13.

*Note:* If some groups finish early, you can have those groups work on *POW 15: A Logical Collection.*

## *Homework 12: Measuring Meals for Alice*

In this assignment, students will need to find decimal approximations for various situations involving Alice.

looks at all techniques

assessment

looking at patterns lends itself better than eating & drinking

# All Roads Lead to Rome

The basic definition for exponential expressions is given in terms of repeated multiplication. For example, $3^5$ means "multiply five 3's together." This gives $3 \cdot 3 \cdot 3 \cdot 3 \cdot 3$, which is 243. Thus, $3^5 = 243$.

In this definition, the **exponent** tells you how many of the **bases** to multiply together. This definition makes sense when the exponent is a positive integer. But you can't interpret zero, negative, or fractional exponents in terms of how many of the bases to multiply. For example, it doesn't make sense to say "multiply negative six 3's together."

*Continued on next page*

In this unit, you have seen other ways to make sense of exponents that are not positive integers.

- You can use the Alice story.
- You can extend a numerical pattern that starts with positive integer exponents.
- You can see what definition will be consistent with the additive law of exponents, which says $A^B \cdot A^C = A^{B+C}$.
- You can make a graph of the equation $y = A^x$ using positive integer values for $x$ and use the graph to estimate $y$ for other values of $x$.

Fortunately, these different approaches lead to the same conclusions. The problems here give you a chance to show how the different methods work.

1. Suppose Alice has base 5 cake and beverage. That is, for each ounce of cake Alice eats, her height is multiplied by 5, and for each ounce of beverage she drinks, her height is multiplied by $\frac{1}{5}$. Explain the meaning of $5^0$ using all four methods described above.

2. The four methods don't necessarily all make sense for every possible exponent. Explain the meaning of each of the exponential expressions here using as many of the four ways as make sense for the particular example. You will need to decide in each case what base of cake or beverage to use.

   a. $3^{-4}$

   b. $2^{1/2}$

   c. $7^{1/3}$

   d. $32^{2/5}$

$5^4 = 625 \div 5$
$5^3$
$5^2 = 125 \div 5$
$25 \div 5$
$5^1 = 5 \div 5$
$5^0 = 1$
$5^{\frac{1}{2}} = \sqrt{5}$

$5^4 = 625$
$5^3 = 125$
$5^2 = 25$
$5^1 = 5$
$5^0 = 1$
$5^{-1} = \frac{1}{5}$
$5^{-2} = \frac{1}{25}$
$5^{-3} = \frac{1}{125}$

$5^4 = 625$
$5^2 = 25$
$5^1 = 5$
$5^{\frac{1}{2}} = \sqrt{5}$

# Homework 12 Measuring Meals for Alice

In this assignment, Alice is using her original base 2 cake and beverage. That is, 1 ounce of cake doubles Alice's height and 1 ounce of beverage halves her height.

Using a scientific calculator, find answers to the nearest tenth of an ounce or tenth of a foot for each of these questions, and explain your answers.

1. If Alice is 1 foot tall, how much cake should she eat to become 10 feet tall?
2. a. If Alice is 1 foot tall, how much cake should she eat to become 100 feet tall?

   b. Compare your result in Question 2a to your answer in Question 1, and discuss the connection between the two problems.
3. If Alice is 9 feet tall and wants to be 3 feet tall, how much beverage should she drink?
4. If Alice is 20 feet tall and she drinks 2.4 ounces of beverage, how tall will she be?

# Turning Exponents Around

If you know what kind of cake and how much cake Alice is eating, then you can figure out what her height will be multiplied by. But what if you only know the *kind* of cake, and you want her to grow by a certain factor? How can you figure out *how much* cake she should eat?

In the final portion of this unit, you'll explore questions like this. You'll learn some special ways to express the answers to such questions, as well as special notation for representing very big and very small numbers.

***This page in the student book introduces Days 13 through 18.***

***Mario Sandoval questions Jason Torres about the graph displayed on his calculator screen.***

# DAY 13 All Roads Lead to Rome

*Students finish their synthesis of the extension of exponentiation.*

## Mathematical Topics

- Continuing to work with noninteger exponents
- Explaining the definitions of exponential expressions when the exponents are not natural numbers

## *Outline of the Day*

### In Class

1. Discuss *Homework 12: Measuring Meals for Alice*
   - Have students represent each problem using an equation with exponents
2. Continued work on *All Roads Lead to Rome* (from Day 12)
3. Discuss *All Roads Lead to Rome*
   - Have students share different ways to explain the extension of exponentiation

### At Home

*Homework 13: Sending Alice to the Moon*

## 1. Discussion of *Homework 12: Measuring Meals for Alice*

You might ask students to discuss the homework in groups and decide on answers. Then have the diamond card member from various groups report.

- *Question 1*

Students should find that the answer to Question 1 (to the nearest tenth) is 3.3 ounces. Before getting into the relationship between this and the next problem, be sure to get an explanation of where this answer comes from.

The presenter might see it as the solution to the equation $2^x = 10$. Presumably, students will have found the numerical value by guess-and-check. (The concept of logarithms will be introduced on Day 14.)

*Note:* If the class had difficulty solving the problem, you can begin by asking for a very rough approximation. For example, ask, "Between which two whole numbers does the answer lie, and why?"

- *Question 2*

The main focus here should be on the connection between this question and Question 1. Students should be able to explain, perhaps with some prompting from you, why the answer to Question 2 should be exactly twice that for Question 1.

Try to get a variety of explanations. Here are two approaches that students might use, one based on the Alice metaphor and one based on laws of exponents.

- If eating 3.3 ounces of cake multiplies Alice's height by 10 (as found in Question 1), then eating this amount twice will multiply her height by 10 and then by 10 again. Therefore, eating 6.6 ounces multiplies her height by 100.
- The answer from Question 1 means that $2^{3.3}$ is approximately equal to 10. That means that $2^{6.6} = 2^{3.3 + 3.3} = 2^{3.3} \cdot 2^{3.3} \approx 10 \cdot 10 = 100$.

- *Questions 3 and 4*

If students have given clear explanations for Questions 1 and 2, you may choose to discuss Questions 3 and 4 only briefly.

In Question 3, Alice should drink about 1.6 ounces of beverage. In Question 4, Alice will become about 3.8 feet tall.

## 2. Continued Work on *All Roads Lead to Rome*

Students may need additional time to work on this activity before beginning presentations. It is more important to give groups enough time to address each problem as completely as possible than to have a whole-class discussion of the ideas.

Remind students that they do not have to explain every problem all four ways. If they feel they are getting bogged down with a particular explanation of a particular problem, then they should move on and come back to it later.

## 3. Discussion of *All Roads Lead to Rome*

As noted earlier, the goal of this activity is for students to review and use the models they have developed for understanding the definitions for zero, negative, and fractional exponents. They should see the rationale for the definition of expressions with exponents that are not whole numbers. With a variety of models available, they will be better able to use one of them to reconstruct these definitions if they forget them.

While this assignment should review the different approaches, it is not intended to lead to a full-blown lesson on each problem. If time is short, discussion of Questions 2c and 2d can be omitted.

## *Homework 13: Sending Alice to the Moon*

This assignment will provide a useful context for introducing the concept of logarithms. Students are expected to solve these problems involving powers of 10 using guess-and-check on their scientific calculators.

# Homework 13 Sending Alice to the Moon

1. Alice has just discovered base 10 cake and is delighted with how powerful it is. One day, after nibbling on the cake, Alice realized that she was 1 mile tall. Having her head up in the sky got her thinking about space travel, and she decided it would be nice to visit the moon, which is about 239,000 miles from the earth.

   How many more ounces of base 10 cake should Alice eat so that the top of her head just touches the moon? Give your answer to the nearest hundredth of an ounce.

2. After her head reached the moon, Alice continued to eat cake until her head reached the planet Pluto, which at that time was approximately 3,670,000,000 miles from the earth. But she forgot to keep track of how many ounces of cake she had eaten to get that tall.

   How many ounces of base 10 beverage must she drink in order to return to a height of 1 mile? Give your answer to the nearest hundredth of an ounce.

DAY 14

# Sending Alice to the Moon

Students are introduced to logarithms through the Alice metaphor.

## Mathematical Topics

- Solving exponential equations
- Introducing logarithms
- Finding base 10 logarithms on calculators

## Outline of the Day

### In Class

1. Discuss *Homework 13: Sending Alice to the Moon*
   - Save the answers for use in the introduction to logarithms
2. Introduce logarithms
   - Bring out that many "Alice questions" are asking for a missing exponent
   - Introduce the terminology and notation of logarithms
   - Emphasize the importance of base 10 logarithms
3. Negative logarithms
   - Bring out that numbers between 0 and 1 have negative logarithms

### At Home

*Homework 14: Alice on a Log*

## 1. Discussion of *Homework 13: Sending Alice to the Moon*

The questions in *Homework 13: Sending Alice to the Moon* are similar to those in *Homework 12: Measuring Meals for Alice.* For example, in Question 1 of *Homework 12: Measuring Meals for Alice,* students needed to solve the equation $2^x = 10$. In Question 1 of *Homework 13: Sending Alice to the Moon,* they needed to solve the equation $10^x = 239{,}000$.

Unless students had trouble with last night's homework, you can have brief presentations on each question. You might start by having presenters tell the class between what two integers the answer lies, as a way of conveying a sense of what the questions are asking.

Save the answers to these questions for use in the discussion of logarithms that follows.

In Question 1, Alice needs about 5.38 ounces of cake. In Question 2, Alice needs about 9.56 ounces of beverage.

## 2. Introducing Logarithms

Bring out that the questions in last night's homework and Questions 1 through 3 in *Homework 12: Measuring Meals for Alice* were all quite similar. That is, they all ask what power to raise a particular base to in order to get a certain result. Explain that this type of question gets asked a lot, in many different contexts, so people have come up with special terminology and notation to deal with it.

Inform students that the solution to the equation $10^x = 239{,}000$ (from last night's Question 1) is represented by the expression

$$\log_{10} 239{,}000$$

Tell them that this expression is read as "log, base 10, of 239,000" (or as "log of 239,000 to the base 10"), and that "log" is an abbreviation for **logarithm.**

*"What do you think the numerical value of $\log_{10} 239{,}000$ is?"*

Then ask students what they think the numerical value of this expression is. If necessary, go back to the equation that this number solves or to the homework question from which the equation came. (If the homework answers aren't posted, have students consult their own homework papers.)

*"What would this number mean to Alice?"*

Ask them what this number would mean to Alice. They should be able to articulate that it tells them the amount of base 10 cake Alice needs to eat in order to multiply her height by 239,000.

### • *Some simple examples*

*"What does $\log_2 8$ mean to Alice or as an exponential equation?"*

Ask students what they think $\log_2 8$ means both to Alice and as an exponential equation. They should see that the expression represents how much base 2 cake Alice must eat to multiply her height by 8 and that it also represents the solution to the exponential equation $2^x = 8$.

Either from the Alice situation or from the equation, they should see that $\log_2 8$ equals 3. Write this equation on the board, and have someone recite it aloud as a way to review how to read logarithm expressions.

You can ask students to make up some logarithm expressions of their own and interpret them in terms of exponents. They should be able to articulate that an expression like $\log_a b$ represents "the power you raise $a$ to in order to get $b$." That is, it represents the solution for $x$ in the equation $a^x = b$.

Also ask students what the expression $\log_a b$ means in Alice's situation. They should see that $a$ describes the type of cake (so we read the "$a$ portion" of the expression as "base $a$") and $b$ describes what is happening to Alice's height. That is, this expression answers the question, "How much base $a$ cake should Alice eat for her height to be multiplied by $b$?"

## • *Other examples of special notation to solve equations*

***"Where else is special notation used to represent the solution to an equation?"***

Ask students if they can think of other examples in which special notation is used to represent the solution to an equation. For example, we represent the answer to the equation $x^2 = 239{,}000$ by the notation

$$\sqrt{239{,}000}$$

which doesn't, in itself, tell you what the answer "is equal to." It's simply a way of naming the answer. Similarly, the solution to the equation $x^3 = 239{,}000$ is represented as

$$\sqrt[3]{239{,}000}$$

You might point out that notation like this is especially useful for representing the exact value of expressions. For instance, the solutions to the equation $x^2 = 2$ have no exact finite decimal expression, so the best way to express them exactly is to write them as $\sqrt{2}$ and $-\sqrt{2}$.

*Note:* This is a good time to remind students that every positive number has two square roots and to tell them that the square-root symbol itself represents only the *positive* square root.

If you want to give students a more elementary example, you can ask what equation the expression $50 \div 6$ is the solution for. Students should see that this represents the solution to the equation $6x = 50$ and that, more generally, every division problem represents the solution to a multiplication equation. In a sense, the notation for division was invented as a shorthand for representing such multiplication equations, just as the notation for roots and logarithms was invented to represent the solutions to two types of exponential equations.

## • *Base 10 logarithms are special*

Tell students that because our number system is a base 10 system, logarithms for base 10 are widely used, and most calculators have a key that gives base 10 logarithms.

Have students find some base 10 logarithms on their graphing calculators and also explore how this is done on their scientific calculators. You can begin by having them verify their answer to Question 1 from last night's homework. *Note:* For some calculators, you hit the log key and then enter the number; on others, you enter the number and then hit the log key. The procedure is generally analogous to that used for square roots, reciprocals, and so on.

You can mention that logarithms to other whole-number bases are rarely used and that they are mentioned in this unit only to provide more varied examples of the meaning of logarithms. Point out that for whole-number bases other than 10, students cannot get the logarithm from a single key, so they should use guess-and-check, as they probably did for base 10 on last night's homework.

*Note:* In the Year 3 unit *Small World, Isn't It?,* students will learn about the special base called *e* and about natural logarithms. Except for an occasional problem to emphasize the meaning of logarithms, students will not be working in IMP with logarithms other than base 10 or base *e*. Therefore, there is no particular reason for them to learn formulas for computing logarithms for other bases.

- ***Estimating base 10 logarithms***

***"If the base 10 logarithm of a number is between 4 and 5, how big is the number?"***

To clarify the significance of using base 10 logarithms, you can ask a question like, "If the base 10 logarithm of a number is between 4 and 5, how big is the number?"

***As a hint: "Between what values should the given number be?"***

As needed, let students experiment with this. As a hint, ask what values the given number should lie between. This should help them see that the number is between $10^4$ and $10^5$ (that is, at least 10,000 and less than 100,000), which means that it is a five-digit number. It may take several examples for them to make the connection between the size of the logarithm and the number of digits.

***"Between what two whole numbers is the logarithm of 273,189?"***

Then turn the process around and have students estimate the logarithm of a given whole number, asking questions such as, "Between what two whole numbers is the logarithm of 273,189?" Students should see that because this is a six-digit number, its logarithm must be between 5 and 6. (Be sure students realize that this principle applies only to logarithms using base 10.)

Work your way down to numbers between 1 and 10—that is, to one-digit numbers—as preparation for the discussion of logarithms for numbers between 0 and 1. Students should see that a one-digit number has a base 10 logarithm between 0 and 1.

## 3. Negative Logarithms

***"What's the approximate value of $\log_{10} 0.25$?"***

As indicated in the previous paragraph, you can build on the pattern students have just seen by asking about the base 10 logarithms for numbers between 0 and 1. You may find it best to begin with a specific example. For instance, ask students to estimate $\log_{10} 0.25$. Emphasize that you only want them to tell you between what two integers the answer lies.

Students may see intuitively that the answer should be between -1 and 0. If not, you might go back to the pattern established for large whole numbers and ask a question like this:

> *If a number between 10 and 100 has a logarithm between 1 and 2, and a number between 1 and 10 has a logarithm between 0 and 1, what would you expect for the logarithm of a number between 0.1 and 1?*

In any case, you should be able to establish that $\log_{10} 0.25$ is negative.

Ask students to find $\log_{10} 0.25$ more precisely on their calculators. If they do this using the base 10 logarithm key (and get approximately -0.6), ask how they could confirm this result using exponents. The goal here is to get them to recognize that the statement $\log_{10} 0.25 \approx -0.6$ is equivalent to the statement $10^{-0.6} \approx 0.25$.

***"What does $\log_{10} 0.001$ mean in terms of exponents?"***

You might then ask a question like "What does $\log_{10} 0.001$ mean in terms of exponents?" As needed, help students rephrase this as something like "What is the solution to the equation $10^x = 0.001$?" Then have students find the numerical value of $x$. Solving this equation may require a review of negative exponents, which would be useful in any case.

Continue with similar examples to remind students that powers of 10 with negative integer exponents are almost as easy to compute as powers of 10 with positive integer exponents.

Don't get too bogged down in details here. The primary goal is for students to see that numbers between 0 and 1 have negative logarithms and that the smaller the number, the "more negative" the logarithm.

## • *Logarithms of negative numbers?*

***"What is $\log_{10} -2.7$?"***

Take this opportunity to bring out that only positive numbers have logarithms. You might ask about a specific example, such as $\log_{10} -2.7$. If students try to do this on a calculator, they should get an error message.

***"Why doesn't -2.7 have a base 10 logarithm?"***

Ask why they get an error message and why -2.7 doesn't have a base 10 logarithm. If necessary, ask them to write an appropriate exponential equation. They should see that they are trying to solve the equation $10^x = -2.7$. They should also see that this equation has no solution, because exponential expressions with base 10 (or any other positive base) give only positive values.

## • *Logarithms and the graph of $y = 10^x$*

You can clarify all of these ideas by reference to the graph of the equation $y = 10^x$. Bring out that $y$-values between 0 and 1 on this graph correspond to negative $x$-values and that there are no points on this graph with negative $y$-values. *Note:* The graph of the base 10 logarithm function is discussed on Day 15.

- *The "Alice" approach*

You can follow up the discussion of logarithms for numbers less than 1 by relating the issue of logarithms back to Alice's situation. If needed, review the general idea that asking for a logarithm is similar to asking how much cake Alice should eat.

***"How much base 10 cake should Alice eat to multiply her height by 0.001?"***

Then take one of the examples the class has discussed, such as $\log_{10} 0.001$, and ask how much base 10 cake Alice should eat to multiply her height by 0.001. Students may respond that eating cake will make her bigger, not smaller. If so, use that response to review the idea that drinking the beverage is similar to eating "negative cake."

Based on this principle, students can find $\log_{10} 0.001$ by recognizing that Alice needs to drink 3 ounces of beverage to multiply her height by 0.001 and then interpreting this as being the same as eating "-3 ounces" of cake. Thus, it makes sense to define $\log_{10} 0.001$ as equal to -3.

## Homework 14: Alice on a Log

This assignment uses logarithms in the context of Alice and her cake and beverage.

# Homework 14 Alice on a Log

In this assignment, Alice is thinking about base 10 cake and beverage. If she eats 1 ounce of this kind of cake, her height will be multiplied by 10, and if she drinks 1 ounce of the beverage, her height will be multiplied by $\frac{1}{10}$.

Alice has just heard about logarithms and is all excited. For example, she found out that $\log_{10} 162$ means "the power to which I should raise 10 to get 162."

"How could anyone find that exciting?" you ask.

Well, Alice thinks it sounds much more sophisticated to ask, "What is $\log_{10} 162$?" than to ask, "How many ounces of base 10 cake should I eat in order to grow to 162 times my height?"

1. Between what two whole numbers does the value of $\log_{10} 162$ lie? Explain your answer.
2. For each of these questions, write a logarithm expression that represents the answer and then find the numerical value of the expression.
   a. How many ounces of base 10 cake should Alice eat to grow to 100 times her size?
   b. How many ounces of base 10 cake should Alice eat to grow to 10,000 times her size?
   c. How many ounces of base 10 cake should Alice eat to grow to 50 times her size?
   d. How many ounces of base 10 cake should Alice eat to grow to 2000 times her size?
   e. How many ounces of base 10 beverage should Alice drink to shrink to $\frac{1}{10}$ her size?
   f. How many ounces of base 10 beverage should Alice drink to shrink to $\frac{1}{4}$ her size?

# Graphs of Logarithms

Students examine the graph of the logarithm function.

## Mathematical Topics

- Working with logarithms
- Graphing logarithmic functions

## Outline of the Day

### In Class

1. Discuss *Homework 14: Alice on a Log*
   - Focus on the relationship between the logarithm expressions and exponential equations
2. *Taking Logs to the Axes*
   - Students examine the graphs of logarithm functions
3. Discuss *Taking Logs to the Axes*
   - Examine how the graph changes as the base changes
   - Bring out the symmetrical relationship between the graphs of a logarithm function and its corresponding exponential function

### At Home

*Homework 15: Base 10 Alice*

## 1. Discussion of *Homework 14: Alice on a Log*

Give groups a brief time to come to a consensus on the homework answers. Then have heart card students report on each question.

Ask presenters to include appropriate exponential equations as part of their presentations. For example, on Question 2c, the class should see that the problem is equivalent to asking for the solution to the equation $10^x = 50$, and the presenter should give the expression $\log_{10} 50$ to represent the answer.

On Questions 2e and 2f, students might use either 10 or $\frac{1}{10}$ as the base. For instance, they might interpret Question 2f in either of these ways:

- As asking for the solution to the equation $10^{-x} = \frac{1}{4}$. Then $-x$ is $\log_{10} \frac{1}{4}$, and $x = -\log_{10} \frac{1}{4}$.
- As asking for the solution the equation $\left(\frac{1}{10}\right)^x = \frac{1}{4}$. Then $x = \log_{1/10} \frac{1}{4}$.

Either approach gives approximately 0.60 for $x$, and you may want to try to elicit both approaches.

## 2. *Taking Logs to the Axes*

You don't need to introduce this activity. Simply have groups start in on it, and then bring the class together for discussion when most groups have done at least some work on Question 4.

As groups finish Questions 1a, 1b, and 2, you can choose a group for each question and have them prepare a transparency of the graph, including scales.

## 3. Discussion of *Taking Logs to the Axes*

You can have spade card students present the graphs for Questions 1a, 1b, and 2.

Then let volunteers share their ideas on Questions 3 and 4, comparing the logarithm graphs to one another and to the graphs of the corresponding exponential functions. For instance, they might point out that as the base for a logarithm function gets larger, the portion of the graph for values of $x$ greater than 1 gets "flatter."

If no one points out the symmetrical relationship between the graph of a logarithm function and that of the corresponding exponential function, you can try to elicit this idea by having students identify specific points on each. For example, if students used the point (8, 3) for the graph of $y = \log_2 x$, bring out that this point fits this equation because $2^3 = 8$, which means that (3, 8) is on the graph of the function $y = 2^x$. Using examples like this, help students see that if $(a, b)$ is on the graph of $y = \log_2 x$, then $(b, a)$ is on the graph of $y = 2^x$, and so the two graphs are symmetrical.

## *Homework 15: Base 10 Alice*

This activity is a lead-in to the idea of scientific notation.

# Taking Logs to the Axes

Once Alice found out that $\log_{10} 162$ means "the power to which I should raise 10 to get 162," she got curious about what the graph of a logarithm function would look like.

She realized that there was a different logarithm function for each base. For example, one such function would be defined by the equation $y = \log_2 x$.

Her investigations relied heavily on the fact that the equation $c = \log_a b$ means the same thing as the equation $a^c = b$. Using this relationship allowed her to work with exponential equations, and she was more comfortable with them.

1. In each of parts a and b, choose values for $x$ for which you can easily compute the value of $y$, and plot the resulting points. Choose enough points in each case to allow you to sketch the entire graph.
   a. $y = \log_2 x$
   b. $y = \log_3 x$
2. Use a graphing calculator to draw the graph of the equation $y = \log_{10} x$.
3. Compare the graph of the logarithm function using base 2 with the graphs of logarithm functions using different bases. In general, how does the graph change as the base gets larger? Why?
4. How does the graph of a logarithm function compare to the graph of the corresponding exponential function?

# Homework 15 Base 10 Alice

All the questions in this assignment refer to base 10 cake and beverage.

1. For each of the quantities shown below, find Alice's height after eating that amount of cake. In each case, assume that she starts at a height of 5 feet.

   a. 4 ounces

   b. 8 ounces

   c. 13 ounces

2. If Alice eats a whole number of ounces of cake and starts from a height of 5 feet, what do you know about the possible heights she can grow to?

3. Suppose Alice is 5 feet tall and wants to know how many ounces of cake she needs to eat to become 50,000,000,000 feet tall. (That's 50 billion feet, which is roughly 10 million miles.) What shortcut can you use in answering her question?

4. Pick three different whole numbers of ounces of beverage for Alice to drink, and find her height after consuming each amount. Assume in each case that she starts out 5 feet tall.

5. Find a simple rule for writing Alice's final height for situations like those you made up in Question 4. Your rule should deal specifically with the case of whole-number ounces of beverage.

# Day 16 Scientific Notation

Students learn scientific notation as a way of expressing very large and very small numbers.

## Mathematical Topics

- Introducing scientific notation
- Introducing order of magnitude

## Outline of the Day

### In Class

1. Discuss *Homework 15: Base 10 Alice*
   - Focus on the importance of powers of 10 in expressing the answers to Questions 1-3
2. Introduce scientific notation
   - Emphasize the importance of having a standard form
   - Introduce the term **order of magnitude**
   - Have students explore how to use scientific notation on calculators
   - Discuss scientific notation for numbers between 0 and 1

### At Home

*Homework 16: Warming Up to Scientific Notation*

*Note:* If you plan to show the video *Powers of Ten* tomorrow, you should arrange to have a video playback machine available.

## 1. Discussion of *Homework 15: Base 10 Alice*

The primary purpose of the homework discussion is to serve as a lead-in to scientific notation. We suggest that you discuss Questions 1 through 3, introduce scientific notation for numbers greater than 1, and then use Questions 4 and 5 to introduce scientific notation for numbers between 0 and 1.

Give groups a few minutes to discuss their results, and then bring the class together for a discussion.

### • *Question 1*

Let volunteers give and explain their answers to the different parts of Question 1. For Question 1c, it would be good to get both "50 trillion" and "5 with 13 zeroes after it" as ways of describing the answer.

***"How could you write your answers to Question 1 using exponents?"***

Ask students how they could write their answers to Question 1 using exponents. For example, they should be able to write the answer to Question 1c as $5 \cdot 10^{13}$. Point out that this is much easier to write and to work with than the written-out value, 50,000,000,000,000.

### • *Questions 2 and 3*

Next, have one or two students give their answers to Questions 2 and 3. The goal of these questions is to get statements involving powers of 10 and "counting zeroes." For example, a student might answer Question 2 by saying that the height Alice grows to must be 5 times a particular power of 10 or that it must be a 5 followed by a number of zeroes.

***"How would you write 25,000 as a whole number times a power of 10?"***

To solidify this basic idea, ask students to express a variety of numbers using powers of 10. For example, ask how to write 25,000 as a whole number times a power of 10. Solicit more than one answer. For instance, you might get both $25 \cdot 10^3$ and $250 \cdot 10^2$.

***"What does each of these expressions mean in terms of an initial height for Alice and eating a whole number of ounces of base 10 cake?"***

Connect these expressions with the Alice situation by asking what initial height and amount of base 10 cake is represented by each expression. For example, $25 \cdot 10^3$ could represent a starting height of 25 feet and eating 3 ounces of cake.

Bring out that each different way to write a given number as a whole number times a power of 10 also represents a different starting height and amount of cake. This is also a good time to bring out that certain combinations involve initial heights that are not whole numbers. For example, help students to see that 25,000 could also represent a starting height of 2.5 feet and eating 4 ounces of cake.

## 2. Scientific Notation

The introduction to scientific notation described here is based on the assumption that students have little or no previous exposure to the concept. Because you may have students who do know something about scientific notation, begin by asking if anyone is familiar with the term *scientific notation*. If you get a positive response, you can continue the discussion by having volunteers describe what they know. Then build on that foundation to elicit any key concepts not introduced.

Use the homework discussion as a lead-in to the idea of scientific notation. Tell students that it is useful in mathematics and science to have a standard way of writing numbers using powers of 10, and that the standard way is like having Alice start at a height of at least 1 foot and less than 10 feet. That is, we write the number as a number between 1 and 10 times an integer power of 10.

***"How would you write 162,000 in this standard form?"***

Ask the students how they would write 162,000 in this standard form. They should be able to come up with the answer $1.62 \cdot 10^5$. Tell them that this is called **scientific notation** and that, for convenience, we will refer to the notation 162,000 as "ordinary" notation. (Clarify that "ordinary" notation is only an informal term we are using.)

Note: There are no standard names for the two components of scientific notation, such as 1.62 and $10^5$ in our example. You might refer to these components informally as the "number part" and the "power-of-ten part."

- ***Order of magnitude***

Tell students that in science and other disciplines, we often want a very rough idea of how big something is. The exponent in the scientific notation of the number helps with this approximation.

Two numbers that have the same exponent when written in scientific notation or that differ from each other by a *factor* of less than 10 are said to have the same **order of magnitude.** For example, the number of people in California (about 29 million) has the same order of magnitude as the number of people in New York State (about 18 million), because both of these numbers would be written in scientific notation as $a \cdot 10^7$, where $a$ is a number between 1 and 10.

On the other hand, the population of New York State has a different order of magnitude from either the population of the whole United States (about 250 million, or $2.5 \cdot 10^8$) or the population of Nevada (about 1.2 million, or $1.2 \cdot 10^6$).

- ***Scientific notation on the calculator***

Have students take some time to explore the use of scientific notation on their graphing calculators and scientific calculators. Point out that many calculators use notation such as 3E5 as a shorthand for $3 \cdot 10^5$.

- ***Questions 4 and 5 of "Homework 15: Base 10 Alice"***

Return to Questions 4 and 5 of the homework. You may need to be more careful than in Questions 1 through 3 to be sure that the numerical answers are clearly understood. For example, students should be able to explain why, if Alice starts at 5 feet tall and drinks 4 ounces of base 10 beverage, she ends up 0.0005 feet tall.

Ask students to articulate the mathematics involved in this rewriting. Focus their attention on the fact that moving the decimal point one place within a number changes the place values for each of the digits—specifically, changing the number by a factor of 10 or $\frac{1}{10}$, depending on the direction of the move.

- *Writing decimals using powers of 10*

***"How would you write the number 0.0005 using a power of 10?"***

Ask students how to write a number like 0.0005 using a power of 10. The context of Questions 4 and 5 may elicit the answer $5 \cdot \left(\frac{1}{10}\right)^4$. If you get this response, you can acknowledge that this is equal to 0.0005, but state that you want students to use 10 instead of $\frac{1}{10}$ as the base. This may require some reminders about negative exponents and the idea that beverage is like "negative cake." Thus, students should be able to express the result of starting at 5 feet tall and drinking 4 ounces of beverage with the expression $5 \cdot 10^{-4}$.

Go through a series of beverage problems similar to those for cake, such as asking how Alice might end up being 0.0035 feet tall. Students should see that she could have started at 35 feet tall and drunk 4 ounces of beverage, or started at 3.5 feet tall and drunk 3 ounces of beverage, and so on.

Ask students how they think a height of 0.0035 feet should be written using scientific notation. They should recognize that $3.5 \cdot 10^{-3}$ is the standard form.

## *Homework 16: Warming Up to Scientific Notation*

This is a straightforward assignment on the use of scientific notation.

# Homework 16 Warming Up to Scientific Notation

Scientific notation may be a new way for you to express numbers. It often takes some practice to get used to working with scientific notation, but it's worth the effort because many ideas in mathematics and science are expressed using this special way of writing numbers.

This homework assignment gives you several ways to get accustomed to scientific notation.

1. Write each of these numbers in scientific notation.

   a. 34,200

   b. 0.0034

*Continued on next page*

2. Write each of these numbers in ordinary notation.

   a. $4.2 \cdot 10^5$

   b. $7.503 \cdot 10^{-2}$

3. Each of the next series of problems gives a product or quotient of two numbers written in scientific notation. Find the numerical value of each result *without using a calculator*, and write your final answers in scientific notation.

   a. $(3 \cdot 10^4) \cdot (2 \cdot 10^7)$

   b. $(5 \cdot 10^5) \cdot (7 \cdot 10^{-2})$

   c. $(7 \cdot 10^8) \div (2 \cdot 10^3)$

   d. $(9 \cdot 10^3) \div (3 \cdot 10^{-4})$

   e. $(6 \cdot 10^{-3}) \div (2 \cdot 10^{-8})$

   f. $(2 \cdot 10^5) \div (4 \cdot 10^3)$

4. Based on the examples in Question 3, develop some general principles for multiplying and dividing numbers written in scientific notation. Make up more examples as needed, and illustrate your rules.

5. a. Figure out and describe how to *enter* numbers in scientific notation on your own scientific calculator.

   b. Describe how your scientific calculator *displays* numbers in scientific notation.

# Day 17 Big Numbers

Students continue their work with scientific notation.

## Mathematical Topics

- Working with scientific notation

## Outline of the Day

### In Class

1. Select presenters for tomorrow's discussion of *POW 15: A Logical Collection*
2. Discuss *Homework 16: Warming Up to Scientific Notation*
   - Focus on the arithmetic of working with scientific notation
3. *Big Numbers*
   - Students find approximate answers for problems involving scientific notation
4. Discuss *Big Numbers*
   - Focus on estimation and order of magnitude
5. (Optional) Show the video *Powers of Ten*

### At Home

*Homework 17: An Exponential Portfolio*

**Special Materials Needed**

- (Optional) The video *Powers of Ten* (see the subsection "Materials" in the Overview) and a video playback machine

## 1. POW Presentation Preparation

Presentations of *POW 15: A Logical Collection* are scheduled for tomorrow. Choose three students to make POW presentations, and give them overhead transparencies and pens to take home to use in their preparations.

Because there are three problems in the POW, you may want to ask each presenter to prepare one specific problem.

## 2. Discussion of *Homework 16: Warming Up to Scientific Notation*

Let students go over Questions 1 through 3 in their groups. You need to discuss as a whole class only those problems for which students cannot agree within their groups.

- *Question 4*

Ask for volunteers to share ideas on Question 4. You should be getting ideas like these.

- To multiply numbers in scientific notation, multiply the "number parts" and add the exponents of the "power-of-ten parts."
- To divide numbers in scientific notation, divide the "number parts" and subtract the exponents of the "power-of-ten parts."

Students should realize that after applying these principles, they sometimes need to make an adjustment to standardize their answer. For example, following the first rule for Question 3b gives $35 \cdot 10^3$, but the correct scientific notation is $3.5 \cdot 10^4$.

This discussion will probably lead to some review of the arithmetic of adding and subtracting positive and negative integers.

- *Question 5*

Ask if any students have any questions about how to work with scientific notation on their scientific calculators. If there are questions, you might pair students up to work through the difficulties.

## 3. *Big Numbers*

Students can get right to work on the next activity, *Big Numbers,* without any introduction.

Because tonight's homework is similar to this activity, we suggest that you discuss at least one or two of the problems today, even if groups have not finished the activity. You can have students complete the activity tomorrow in class, or in addition to tonight's homework, if needed.

You may need to give groups hints, or if students seem very frustrated, you may want to do Question 1 as a whole class. Also, if necessary, go over the fact that a kilogram is 1000 grams (Question 5), and that a meter is 1000 millimeters (Question 8).

## 4. Discussion of *Big Numbers*

You can ask the club card members of different groups to present each answer. Students may do these problems in a variety of ways, and it is worthwhile eliciting other approaches after the presentations, at least for a few problems.

### • *Question 1*

Students might answer Question 1 by writing 30 as $3 \cdot 10^1$ and then expressing the answer as the quotient $(3 \cdot 10^1) \div (5 \cdot 10^{-7})$. This would give $0.6 \cdot 10^8$, which can be rewritten in scientific notation as $6 \cdot 10^7$.

Alternatively, students might say that because the computer does a computation in $5 \cdot 10^{-7}$ seconds, it can do $10^7$ computations in 5 seconds. Because 30 seconds is six times as long as 5 seconds, the computer can do $6 \cdot 10^7$ computations in 30 seconds.

### • *Question 2*

On Question 2, you might have students write an expression that represents the answer without actually doing any arithmetic. For example, one could express the number of seconds per year as

$$60 \cdot 60 \cdot 24 \cdot 365$$

which gives the number of gallons per year as

$$(60 \cdot 60 \cdot 24 \cdot 365) \div 76{,}000$$

You can then have students look at ways to estimate this product, such as rewriting it as approximately

$$(6 \cdot 10^1) \cdot (6 \cdot 10^1) \cdot (2 \cdot 10^1) \cdot (4 \cdot 10^2) \div (8 \cdot 10^4)$$

You might note that 24 has been rounded down and that 365 has been rounded up, so there is some balancing out.

Students might multiply $6 \cdot 6$ to get 36, approximate $36 \cdot 2$ as 70 and $70 \cdot 4$ as 300, and then approximate $300 \div 8$ as 40. The powers of 10 combine to give $10^1$, so this gives a final estimate of $40 \cdot 10^1$, which is 400. (A more exact answer is about 415 gallons. If it's a leap year, the answer is just over 416 gallons.)

### • *Questions 3 through 8*

Here are approximate answers to the rest of the problems.

- Question 3: about $2.53 \cdot 10^8$ years (or about 253 million years)
- Question 4: about $13,000
- Question 5: about $5 \cdot 10^{25}$ atoms
- Question 6: about $3.3 \cdot 10^5$ or 330,000 earths
- Question 7: about $3.7 \cdot 10^{17}$ inches
- Question 8: about $4.7 \cdot 10^{15}$ grains of sand (or about 4.7 quadrillion grains of sand)

## 5. Optional: *Powers of Ten* Video

The 9-minute video *Powers of Ten* gives an excellent visual lesson on orders of magnitude, and students generally enjoy it. (If there is no time today, you can show it tomorrow.)

## *Homework 17: An Exponential Portfolio*

Tonight's assignment is the first step toward creating the unit portfolio.

***IMP teachers Maria Ayala-Marshall and Dennis Cavaillé decide which work to include in their own unit portfolios.***

# *Big Numbers*

Scientific notation is sometimes helpful in working with big numbers.

In some of the problems in this activity, you are given information in scientific notation. You can use what you learned in *Homework 16: Warming Up to Scientific Notation* to simplify the computations.

You will probably want to write your answers in scientific notation. But you do not necessarily need to give exact answers for these problems. Use your judgment about the amount of precision that is appropriate in each case.

1. A computer can do a computation in $5 \cdot 10^{-7}$ seconds. How many computations can the computer do in 30 seconds?

2. A leaking faucet drips a drop per second. If there are 76,000 drops of water in a gallon, how many gallons would drip in a year?

*Continued on next page*

3. Measurements show that Europe and Africa are separating from the Americas at a rate of about 1 inch per year. The continents are now about 4000 miles apart. Assuming that the rate has remained constant, how many years has it been since the continents split apart and started drifting?

4. In 1990, the gross national debt of the United States was \$3,233,313,000,000. The 1990 census showed 248,709,873 U.S. citizens. About how many dollars per citizen was the national debt in 1990?

5. One atom of carbon weighs approximately $1.99 \cdot 10^{-23}$ grams. How many atoms are there in a kilogram of carbon?

6. The mass of the earth is $5.98 \cdot 10^{24}$ kg. The mass of the sun is $1.99 \cdot 10^{30}$ kg. Approximately how many earths would it take to have the same mass as the sun?

7. Light travels at a speed of approximately 186,000 miles per second. (That's *very* fast.) A **light-year** is the distance that light travels in a year. Approximately how many inches are there in a light-year?

8. For simplicity, suppose that a grain of sand is a cube that is 0.2 millimeters in each direction. About how many grains of sand packed tightly together would it take to make a beach that is 300 meters long, 25 meters wide, and 5 meters deep?

Questions 1–4 were adapted from problems in *Algebra I,* by Paul A. Foerster, Addison-Wesley Publishing Co., 1990, pp. 404–406. Data in Question 4 taken from *Information Please,* 1996 Almanac, 49th edition, Houghton-Mifflin.

# Homework 17 An Exponential Portfolio

Although you have seen in this unit that exponents don't have to be positive integers, you have also seen many general laws about exponents that are based on the definition of exponentiation as repeated multiplication.

Your task in this assignment is to list all the general laws of exponents that you have studied. Give at least one explanation for each general law. Your explanations may be based on the definition or may use some other approach, such as the "Alice" metaphor or a numerical pattern.

# POW 15 Presentations and Portfolios

Students present POW 15 and compile their portfolios for the unit.

## Mathematical Topics

- Reasoning logically
- Reviewing the unit and preparing portfolios

## Outline of the Day

### In Class

1. Remind students that they will take unit assessments tomorrow and tomorrow night
2. Discuss *Homework 17: An Exponential Portfolio*
3. Presentations of *POW 15: A Logical Collection*
4. *"All About Alice" Portfolio*
   - Students write cover letters and assemble portfolios for the unit

### At Home

Students complete portfolios and prepare for unit assessments

## 1. Reminder: Unit Assessments Tomorrow

Remind students that they will get their in-class and take-home unit assessments tomorrow.

## 2. Discussion of *Homework 17: An Exponential Portfolio*

Let volunteers offer general laws about exponents. As each law is suggested, have the rest of the class decide if the statement is true. Elicit as many different explanations as possible.

## 3. Presentations of *POW 15: A Logical Collection*

Have the presenters discuss the individual problems, and let students comment on the presentations and give any alternative approaches that they found. Help students focus the discussion on the *explanations* for the answers, rather than on the answers themselves.

If some of your students were unable to solve *POW 11: A Hat of a Different Color* (in *Cookies*), you may want to suggest that they revisit it now and apply their additional experience with logical reasoning.

## 4. *"All About Alice" Portfolio*

Tell students to read over the instructions in *"All About Alice" Portfolio* carefully and then take out all of their work from the unit.

They will have begun work on the portfolio as last night's homework, so their main task today is to write their cover letters.

If students do not complete their cover letters, you may want them to take the materials home and finish compiling their portfolios for homework. Be sure that they bring the portfolio back tomorrow with the cover letter as the first item. They should also bring to class any other work that they think will be of help on tomorrow's unit assessments. The remainder of their work can be kept at home.

## Homework: Prepare for Assessments

Students' homework for tonight is to prepare for tomorrow's assessments by reviewing the ideas of the unit.

# "All About Alice" Portfolio

Now that *All About Alice* is completed, it is time to put together your portfolio for the unit. Compiling this portfolio has three parts:

- Writing a cover letter in which you summarize the unit
- Choosing papers to include from your work in this unit
- Discussing your personal growth during the unit

## Cover Letter for "All About Alice"

Look back over *All About Alice* and describe the central theme of the unit and the main mathematical ideas. This description should give an overview of how the key ideas were developed in this unit.

As part of the compilation of your portfolio, you will select some activities that you think were important in developing the key ideas. Your cover letter should include an explanation of why you are selecting each particular item.

## Selecting Papers from "All About Alice"

Your portfolio from *All About Alice* should contain

- *Homework 17: An Exponential Portfolio*
- *All Roads Lead to Rome*
- A homework or class activity in which you used exponents to solve the problem

*Continued on next page*

- A homework or class activity that involved graphing
- *Homework 8: Negative Reflections*
- A Problem of the Week
  Select one of the two POWs you completed during this unit (*More From Lewis Carroll* or *A Logical Collection*).

## Personal Growth

Your cover letter for *All About Alice* describes how the unit develops. As part of your portfolio, write about your personal development during this unit. You may want to address this question.

> *How do you think you have grown mathematically over your second year of IMP?*

You should include here any other thoughts about your experiences with this unit that you want to share with a reader of your portfolio.

# DAY 19 Final Assessments

*Students do the in-class assessment and can begin work on the take-home assessment.*

## Outline of the Day

### In Class

Introduce assessments

- Students do *In-Class Assessment for "All About Alice"*
- Students begin *Take-Home Assessment for "All About Alice"*

### At Home

Students complete *Take-Home Assessment for "All About Alice"*

**Special Materials Needed**

- *In-Class Assessment for "All About Alice"*
- *Take-Home Assessment for "All About Alice"*

## 1. End-of-Unit Assessments

*Note:* The in-class assessment is intentionally short so that time pressures will not affect students' performance. The IMP *Teaching Handbook* contains general information about the purpose of the end-of-unit assessments and ways to use them.

Tell students that today they will get two tests—one that they will finish in class and one that they can start in class and will be able to finish at home. The take-home part should be handed in tomorrow.

Tell students that they are allowed to use graphing calculators, notes from previous work, and so forth, when they do the assessments. (They will have to do without graphing calculators when they complete the take-home portion at home unless they have their own.)

The assessments are provided separately in Appendix B for you to duplicate.

# In-Class Assessment for "All About Alice"

Seven equations are shown here. Some may be true and some may be false. You have to decide. Do parts a and b for each of the equations.

a. State whether the equation is true.

b. Explain your answer.

- If you think the equation is true, say why. If possible, state and explain a general principle that the equation illustrates.
- If you think the equation is false, change the right side of the equation to make it true, and explain why the new equation is true.

1. $10^5 \cdot 10^{12} = 10^{17}$
2. $\frac{3^8}{3^2} = 3^4$
3. $\sqrt{10^{16}} = 10^4$
4. $(5^2)^3 = 5^6$
5. $\frac{1.4 \cdot 10^8}{0.7 \cdot 10^4} = 2 \cdot 10^4$
6. $5^3 + 5^2 = 5^5$
7. $\log_2 8 = 3$

# Take-Home Assessment for *All About Alice*

## *Part I: Graph It*

1. Sketch the graph of the function $y = 1.5^x$ from $x = -3$ to $x = 3$. Label at least five points with their coordinates.

2. Explain and show how to use your graph to estimate these values.

   a. $1.5^{-0.5}$

   b. $\log_{1.5} 2$

## *Part II: Far, Far Away*

Give your answers to these questions in scientific notation, and explain clearly how you get them.

3. Light travels very fast, at approximately $1.86 \cdot 10^5$ miles per second. A **light-year** is the distance that light travels in a year.

   a. About how many miles are there in a light-year?

   b. The star Betelgeuse is about $3.6 \cdot 10^{15}$ miles from the earth. About how many light-years is this?

4. An **astronomical unit** is the distance from the earth to the sun, which is approximately $9.3 \cdot 10^7$ miles.

   a. About how many astronomical units from the earth is Betelgeuse?

   b. Which is bigger: an astronomical unit or a light-year? About how many of one equals the other?

# Part III: All Roads Lead to Understanding

The next two equations show how certain expressions with exponents are defined. For each equation, give as many different explanations as you can for why the expressions are defined the way they are. (You should give at least two explanations for each definition.)

5. $4^0 = 1$
6. $5^{-3} = \frac{1}{125}$

# DAY 20 Summing Up

*Students sum up what they learned in the unit and during the year.*

## Mathematical Topics

- Summarizing the unit

## *Outline of the Day*

1. Discuss unit assessments
2. Sum up the unit and the year

*Note:* The assessment discussions and unit summary are presented as if they take place on the day following the assessments, but you may prefer to delay this material until you have looked over students' work on the assessments. These discussion ideas are included here to remind you that some time should be allotted for this type of discussion.

## 1. Discussion of Unit Assessments

You can have students volunteer to explain their work on each of the problems. Encourage questions and alternate explanations from other students.

- *In-class assessment*

You can have diamond card students present different problems, explaining why the statement is true or false and giving a corrected statement as needed.

- *Take-home assessment*

In the discussion of Part I, focus on the use of the graph (Question 2). Question 2b should provide you with a good sense of how well your students understand the connection between exponents and logarithms.

The questions in Part II will give you a sense of how comfortable your class is with scientific notation. Part III will give you guidance on their understanding of the extension of exponentiation to exponents other than positive integers.

# 2. Unit and Year 2 Summary

## • *Summary of "All About Alice"*

***"What have you learned in this unit?"***

Let volunteers share their portfolio cover letters as a way to start a discussion to summarize the unit. Then have students brainstorm to come up with descriptions of what they have learned in the unit. This is a good opportunity to review terminology and to place the unit in a broader mathematics context.

## • *Summary of Year 2*

This is a good opportunity to let students review their entire work for Year 2. You might begin by asking students to name the individual units and have volunteers give a brief description of each. You can then move on to more details, perhaps asking students to list key concepts and the ways they were used to solve the unit problems.

Appendix A

# Supplemental Problems

This appendix contains a variety of additional activities that you can use to supplement the regular unit material. These activities fall roughly into two categories.

- Reinforcements, which are intended to increase students' understanding of and comfort with concepts, techniques, and methods that are discussed in class and that are central to the unit
- Extensions, which allow students to explore ideas beyond the basic unit and which sometimes deal with generalizations or abstractions of ideas that are part of the main unit

The supplemental activities are given here and in the student materials in the approximate sequence in which you might use them in the unit. In the student book, they are placed following the regular materials for the unit. The discussion here makes specific recommendations about how each activity might work within the unit.

For more ideas about the use of supplemental activities in the IMP curriculum, see the IMP *Teaching Handbook*.

- *Inflation, Depreciation, and Alice* (reinforcement)

  This problem can be done as soon as the basic idea of the "Alice" situation is clear. In order to find formulas for Questions 1 and 2, students should recognize that increasing prices by 5 percent is the same as multiplying prices by 1.05; they should have a similar realization for depreciation.

- *More About Rallods* (extension)

  This activity uses the situation in *Homework 6: Rallods in Rednow Land* as the motivation for an investigation of geometric sequences. This supplemental problem can be used any time after the discussion of that homework assignment on Day 7.

- *Exponential Graphing* (reinforcement)

  This problem can be assigned after the Day 11 discussion under the heading "The General Exponential Function."

- *Basic Exponential Questions* (extension)

  This problem can also be assigned any time after the Day 11 discussion under the heading "The General Exponential Function." Question 2 is intentionally trivial (because it involves base 1); Question 3 follows up with a similar, but more complicated, problem.

  Question 4 is quite difficult to solve in general. The only whole-number solutions are the cases in which $X$ is 2 and $Y$ is 4, and vice versa. Students may come up with explanations for why there are no other solutions.

- *Alice's Weights and Measures* (extension)

  This activity focuses on the issues of approximation and error propagation. That is, when a measurement is only an approximation, what impact does it have on computations that make use of that measurement?

  Students should be able to handle this problem once they understand how the general exponential function is defined (after Day 11).

- *A Little Shakes a Lot* (reinforcement)

  Students are often interested in earthquakes, so the Richter scale provides a good way to get them interested in how logarithms work. You can use this activity after the introduction to logarithms on Day 14.

- *Who's Buried in Grant's Tomb?* (extension)

  This activity provides another setting in which students can explore the meaning of logarithms and exponents. It can be used any time after Day 14.

- *Very Big and Very Small* (extension)

  This activity offers students an opportunity to use scientific notation in any context that intrigues them. You can assign the problem after the introduction to scientific notation on Day 16.

# Supplemental Problems

***This page in the student book introduces the supplemental problems.***

Most of the supplemental problems for *All About Alice* continue the focus on exponents and related ideas. Here are some examples.

- *Inflation, Depreciation, and Alice* presents the idea of how changes in prices might involve exponential functions.
- *A Little Shakes a Lot* describes an important use of logarithms.
- *Very Big and Very Small* continues your work with scientific notation.

424 Interactive Mathematics Program

# *Inflation, Depreciation, and Alice*

As you probably have discovered, prices tend to go up over the years. For example, you may know that it used to cost only 10¢ to use a pay phone, but it now costs 20¢ or 25¢.

This sort of rise in costs is called **inflation.** The inflation rate for an item or service is the percentage increase in its price over time. For instance, an annual inflation rate of 5 percent means that prices go up 5 percent each year. (Of course, the rate of inflation is usually not constant.)

1. Suppose that the price of a large jar of peanut butter in 1995 was $3.49.
   a. Using an annual inflation rate of 5 percent, find what the price of this jar of peanut butter will be in the year 2010.
   b. Use your work from part a to come up with a formula that will find the price of the peanut butter $N$ years after 1995.

In many situations, the value of an item decreases over time. For example, a car that was purchased new for $12,000 five years ago may be worth only $5,000 today. This is called **depreciation.**

If an item depreciates at the rate of 10 percent per year, then the item loses 10 percent of its value each year. That is, at the end of each year, its value is 10 percent less than it was at the start of that year.

2. A fitness club purchases a treadmill for $4800. Because of heavy use, the treadmill depreciates 15% per year.
   a. How much will the treadmill be worth in 10 years?
   b. Use your work in part a to come up with a rule for finding the value of the treadmill after $T$ years.
   c. When will the treadmill be worth nothing?
3. What do these problems have to do with *All About Alice?* Describe "Alice" situations that would fit the rules that you found in Questions 1 and 2.

# More About Rallods

## Part I: Counting Rallods

In *Homework 6: Rallods in Rednow Land,* you studied a situation that involved the powers of 2. To solve that problem, the wise advisor in Rednow Land might have liked to have an easy way to find the sum of such powers. Perhaps you can help.

1. Find a general formula, in terms of $n$, for the sum $1 + 2 + 4 + \cdots + 2^n$. You may want to start by investigating some specific examples, choosing small values for $n$.

## Part II: Geometric Sequences

The sequence of powers of 2—that is, 1, 2, 4, 8, 16, and so on—is an example of a **geometric sequence.** A geometric sequence is any sequence of numbers in which each term is a fixed multiple of the previous term. In this example, the multiplier is 2, because each term is twice the one before it.

*Continued on next page*

The multiplier can be any number. For example, if the multiplier is 3 and the first term of the sequence is 1, then the sequence is 1, 3, 9, 27, 81, and so on.

A geometric sequence can have any number as its first term. For example, if the first term is 12 and the multiplier is $\frac{1}{2}$, then the sequence is 12, 6, 3, $1\frac{1}{2}$, and so on.

2. To get started working with these sequences, develop a general formula for finding a given term of a geometric sequence if you know the first term and the multiplier. For instance, if the first term is $a$ and the multiplier is $r$, what is the fourth term? The tenth term? The hundredth term? The $n$th term?

3. Consider sums of terms of geometric sequences that begin with 1.

   a. Examine sums of the form $1 + 3 + 3^2 + \cdots + 3^k$ for different values of $k$. Find a formula for such a sum in terms of $k$.

   b. Look at examples using different multipliers, and try to find formulas similar to those in Question 1 and Question 3a.

   c. Find a general formula for a sum of the form $1 + r + r^2 + \cdots + r^n$. Your answer should be an expression in terms of $r$ and $n$.

4. Consider sums for general geometric sequences, using $a$ to represent the first term and $r$ to represent the multiplier. Your goal is to find a general formula, in terms of $a$, $r$, and $n$, for the sum $a + ar + ar^2 + \cdots + ar^n$. (*Hint:* Think about how such a sum compares with the corresponding sum for the sequence with the same multiplier but whose first term is 1.)

# Exponential Graphing

1. Consider the functions *f*, *g*, and *h* defined by these three equations.

   $f(x) = 2^{(x^2)}$

   $g(x) = 2^{2x}$

   $h(x) = (2^x)^2$

   Investigate the graphs of these three functions, and discuss the ways in which each graph is the same as or different from the other two.

2. Use an In-Out table to graph the function given by the equation $y = -(2^{-0.5x})$.

3. Explain why the function whose equation is $y = 2^{-x}$ has the same graph as the function whose equation is $y = \left(\frac{1}{2}\right)^x$.

4. Graph the function whose equation is $y = (-3)^x$ using only integer values for $x$. Describe and explain the behavior of this graph.

# Basic Exponential Questions

The numerical value of an expression like $a^b$ depends on both the base and the exponent. In these problems, you will explore some patterns involved in varying either the base or the exponent, or both.

Be sure to explain your conclusions using examples.

1. If $n < 0$, which is larger, $2^n$ or $3^n$?
2. If $X < 0$, which is larger, $1^{3X}$ or $1^{3+X}$?
3. Consider the two expressions $2^{5m}$ and $2^{m-1}$.
   a. For which values of $m$ is $2^{5m} > 2^{m-1}$?
   b. For which values of $m$ is $2^{5m} < 2^{m-1}$?
   c. For which values of $m$ is $2^{5m}$ equal to $2^{m-1}$?
4. If $X$ and $Y$ represent the same number, then the expressions $X^Y$ and $Y^X$ will certainly give the same result. But what if $X$ and $Y$ are not equal? Find out what you can about solutions to the equation $X^Y = Y^X$ in which $X$ and $Y$ are not equal.

# Alice's Weights and Measures

When Alice was growing so that her head reached into space, she learned some lessons about approximation.

She decided to visit a star that was 1 quadrillion miles away. (*One quadrillion* means $10^{15}$.) So she adjusted her height to 1 mile, and then ate 15 ounces of base 10 cake. (She didn't have any problem eating that much, because she was a mile tall to begin with.)

Much to her surprise, she was way off her goal when she finished eating. She looked down and saw some cake crumbs lying at her feet. (Her vision was excellent.)

It turned out that she had dropped some of her cake. She had her friend the Mad Hatter weigh the crumbs and discovered that she had actually eaten only 14.99 ounces (instead of exactly 15 ounces).

1. Without using a calculator, guess how far Alice was from the star.
2. Now calculate how far Alice really was from the star.
3. What percentage of Alice's 15 ounces of cake was dropped as crumbs?
4. By what percentage of 1 quadrillion miles did Alice miss her goal?

*Continued on next page*

5. Suppose Alice had not spilled any cake crumbs, but had been a little careless when she measured her initial height. Specifically, suppose that she was really 0.99 miles tall, rather than 1 mile, but that she did eat exactly 15 ounces of base 10 cake.

    a. Without using a calculator, guess how far Alice was from the star in this case.

    b. Now calculate how far Alice really was from the star.

    c. By what percentage was Alice's initial height measurement off from her estimate of 1 mile?

    d. By what percentage of 1 quadrillion miles did Alice miss her goal?

# A Little Shakes a Lot

One of the most familiar uses of logarithms (at least in some places) is the **Richter scale,** which is a numerical way of describing the size of an earthquake. Somewhat simplified, the equation used to get the Richter scale number of an earthquake is

$$R = \log_{10} a$$

where $R$ is the Richter scale number and $a$ is the amplitude or amount of the ground motion, as measured on a seismograph.

In order to give intuitive meaning to Richter scale numbers, you need to have some points of reference. For example, an earthquake that measures 4.0 on the Richter scale is barely perceptible outside its immediate center. In contrast, the great San Francisco earthquake of 1906 measured 8.3 on the Richter scale.

1. The Richter scale numbers make it sound as if the 1906 earthquake was only about twice as big as an earthquake that can hardly be felt. But, in fact, that isn't the case at all. Show this by figuring out the answers to these questions.
   a. How many times as much ground motion does an 8.3 quake have compared to a 4.0 quake?
   b. What Richter measurement would represent a quake that has twice the ground motion of one that measures 4.0 on the Richter scale?
   c. What Richter measurement would represent a quake that has half the ground motion of one that measures 8.3 on the Richter scale?
2. The 1989 Loma Prieta earthquake in California was measured at about 7.1 on the Richter scale. In numerical terms, how did the amount of its ground motion compare to that of the 1906 earthquake?

# *Who's Buried in Grant's Tomb?*

There's a silly old riddle that asks, "Who's buried in Grant's tomb?" Based on this riddle, people sometimes use the phrase "Grant's tomb question" to describe any problem that contains its own answer.

(Another example is the question, "What was the color of George Washington's white horse?")

1. Here are some questions about exponents and logarithms that might be called Grant's tomb questions. Be sure to explain your answers.
   a. What is the cube root of $17^3$?
   b. What is the value of $\log_5(5^8)$?
   c. What is the value of $7^{(\log_7 83)}$?
   d. For what value of $x$ is $\log_x(2^{11})$ equal to 11?
   e. How can you simplify the expression $\left(\sqrt[6]{162}\right)^6$?
2. Make up some Grant's tomb questions of your own. (They don't have to involve exponents and logarithms.)

By the way, the original Grant's tomb riddle is actually a trick question. The elaborate monument in New York City contains both the body of Ulysses S. Grant—the eighteenth president of the United States—and that of his wife, Julia Grant. Most people don't realize that she's also buried there.

# Very Big and Very Small

For this activity, you need to think of two situations in which there are numerical questions you would like to investigate.

- The first situation should involve *very large* numbers.
- The second situation should involve *very small* numbers.

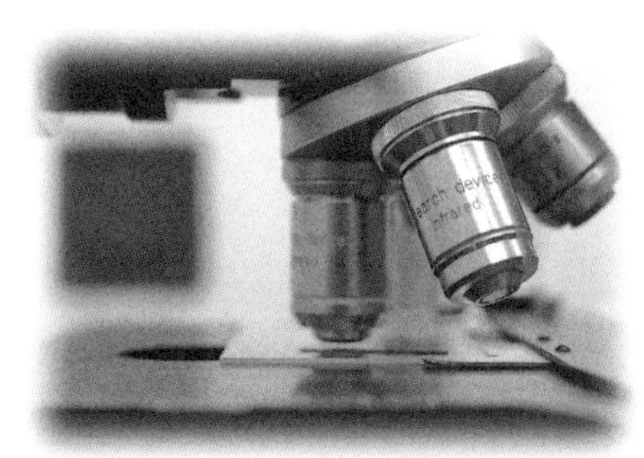

You can use the examples in *Big Numbers* for ideas.

Write a report on each of your situations. You can use reference books or actual measurements and estimates to get the data for your reports.

*Note:* You may want to check with your teacher about the suitability of your situations and numerical questions.

This appendix contains these materials for the unit:

- The diagram comparing the graphs of $y = x + 1$ and $y = 2^x$ (for making a transparency to use on Day 10)
- The in-class and take-home assessments for the unit

This appendix also contains a final assessment for the second semester of Year 2, suggested for students in schools using a traditional semester schedule. This assessment is designed on the assumption that in the second semester, your class will have completed the third unit of the year (*Do Bees Build It Best?*) as well as the fourth and fifth units (*Cookies* and *All About Alice*).

This semester assessment is not intended to be a comprehensive test of the material in these units, but focuses instead on some essential ideas. We recommend that you give students two hours to work on the semester assessment so they can complete it without time pressure, and that you allow them to use graphing calculators and to have access to their textbooks and notes (including portfolios).

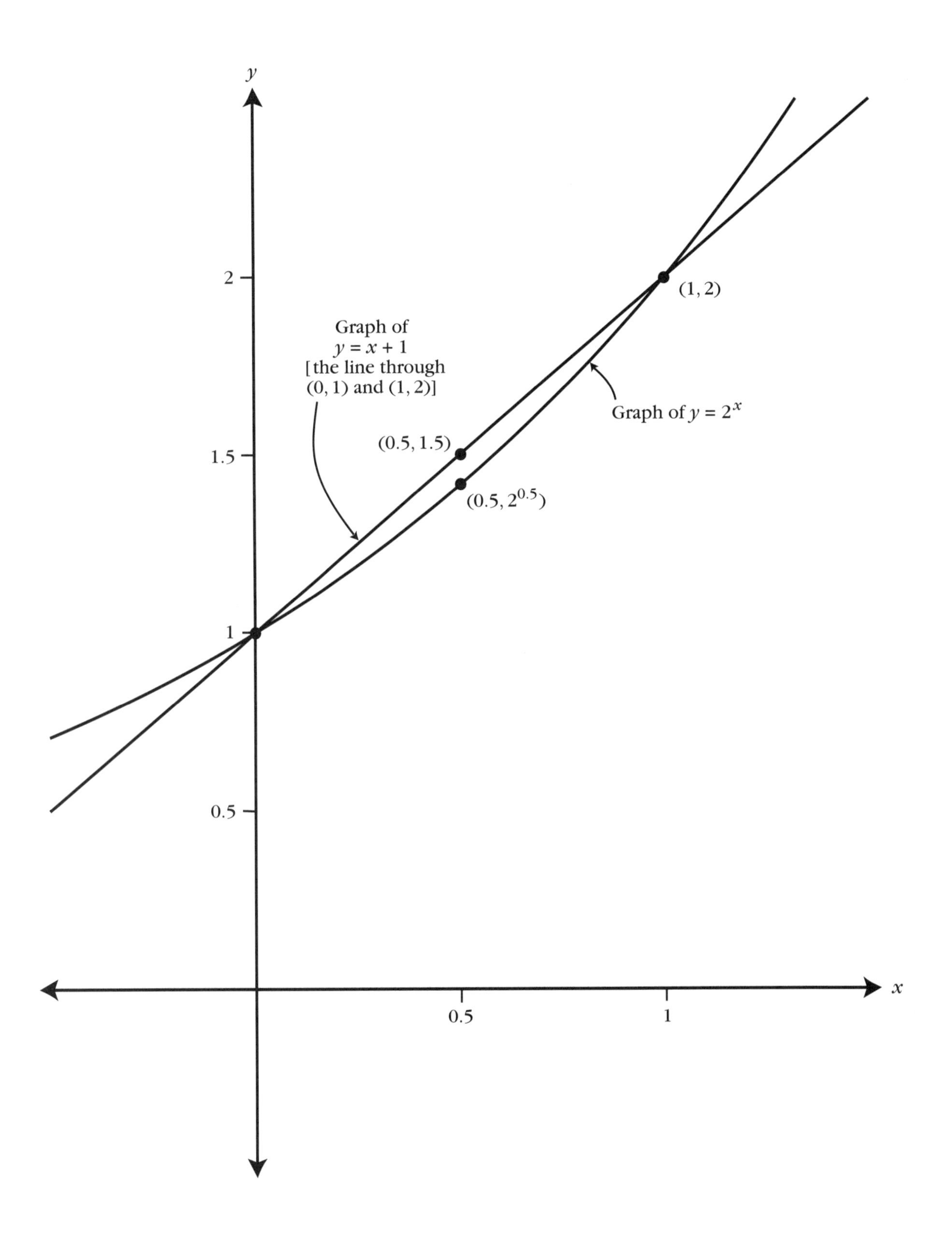
y
2
1.5
1
0.5
x
0.5
1
(1, 2)
Graph of
$y = x + 1$
[the line through
(0, 1) and (1, 2)]
Graph of $y = 2^x$
(0.5, 1.5)
$(0.5, 2^{0.5})$

# In-Class Assessment for "All About Alice"

Seven equations are shown here. Some may be true and some may be false. You have to decide. Do parts a and b for each of the equations.

a. State whether the equation is true.

b. Explain your answer.

- If you think the equation is true, say why. If possible, state and explain a general principle that the equation illustrates.
- If you think the equation is false, change the right side of the equation to make it true, and explain why the new equation is true.

1. $10^5 \cdot 10^{12} = 10^{17}$

2. $\frac{3^8}{3^2} = 3^4$

3. $\sqrt{10^{16}} = 10^4$

4. $(5^2)^3 = 5^6$

5. $\frac{1.4 \cdot 10^8}{0.7 \cdot 10^4} = 2 \cdot 10^4$

6. $5^3 + 5^2 = 5^5$

7. $\log_2 8 = 3$

# Take-Home Assessment for *All About Alice*

## *Part I: Graph It*

1. Sketch the graph of the function $y = 1.5^x$ from $x = -3$ to $x = 3$. Label at least five points with their coordinates.

2. Explain and show how to use your graph to estimate these values.

   a. $1.5^{-0.5}$

   b. $\log_{1.5} 2$

## *Part II: Far, Far Away*

Give your answers to these questions in scientific notation, and explain clearly how you get them.

3. Light travels very fast, at approximately $1.86 \cdot 10^5$ miles per second. A **light-year** is the distance that light travels in a year.

   a. About how many miles are there in a light-year?

   b. The star Betelgeuse is about $3.6 \cdot 10^{15}$ miles from the earth. About how many light-years is this?

4. An **astronomical unit** is the distance from the earth to the sun, which is approximately $9.3 \cdot 10^7$ miles.

   a. About how many astronomical units from the earth is Betelgeuse?

   b. Which is bigger: an astronomical unit or a light-year? About how many of one equals the other?

 

# *Part III: All Roads Lead to Understanding*

The next two equations show how certain expressions with exponents are defined. For each equation, give as many different explanations as you can for why the expressions are defined the way they are. (You should give at least two explanations for each definition.)

5. $4^0 = 1$
6. $5^{-3} = \frac{1}{125}$

 

# IMP Year 2
# Second Semester Assessment

## I. Cheerful Cows

The Cheerful Cow Dairy Company has a new container on the market. It is a right prism with a base that is an equilateral triangle. The sides of the base are 5 inches in length and the container is 10 inches tall.

1. How much cardboard is needed to build each container? (Assume that there is no wasted cardboard and no overlap.)
2. What is the volume of each container?
3. If a cow's udders can be emptied at a rate of 25 squirts per minute and each squirt contains 0.5 cubic inches of milk, how long will it take a milker to fill one of the new containers?

 

# II. Power Power

4. Examine the In-Out table at the right.

   a. Write a rule for the table.

   b. Make a graph based on the table.

   c. Use your graph to find the approximate value for the Out when the In is 2.5. Explain your reasoning.

| In | Out |
|---|---|
| -3 | $\frac{1}{27}$ |
| -2 | $\frac{1}{9}$ |
| -1 | $\frac{1}{3}$ |
| 0 | 1 |
| 1 | 3 |
| 2 | 9 |
| 3 | 27 |

5. Find the value of each of these expressions and justify your answers. That is, explain why each expression has the value it does.

   a. $\log_3 9$

   b. $5^0$

6. Write each of these numbers in standard scientific notation.

   a. 38,000

   b. 0.00506

   c. $0.16 \cdot 10^4$

# III. Mini-POW

7. Solve this problem and then write up your results in POW style, describing your process, solution, and extensions or generalizations.

   *You are going to the baseball game with your younger sibling. When you get there, you find an empty row with 30 seats. In order to save room for friends, you decide to leave at least three empty seats between the two of you.*

   *Given this requirement, how many different choices are there for where you and your sibling can sit in the row? Explain your answer.*

 

# IV. Equalities and Inequalities

8. Ling is in charge of getting sodas for choir members to drink after rehearsal. Each of the 34 members gets one soda, but people often complain that there are too many or two few diet sodas.

   When Denzel was in charge last week, there were no complaints, so Ling asked Denzel how many sodas he got of each type. Unfortunately, he didn't remember, so she looked in the choir account book and found that Denzel spent $24.51. Ling knows that diet sodas cost 69¢ each and that regular sodas are 74¢ each. Figure out how many of each Denzel bought by setting up and solving a system of equations.

9. Consider the inequality $2x + 3y \leq 10$.

   a. Graph this inequality, and explain *in detail* your method and reasoning in constructing your graph. Be sure to explain the relationship between the graph and the inequality.

   b. Make up a real-life problem that the inequality could be used to represent.

This is the glossary for all five units of IMP Year 2.

*Absolute growth* The growth of a quantity, usually over time, found by subtracting the initial value from the final value. Used in distinction from **percentage growth.**

*Additive law of exponents* The mathematical principle which states that the equation

$$A^B \cdot A^C = A^{B+C}$$

holds true for all numbers $A$, $B$, and $C$ (as long as the expressions are defined).

*Altitude of a parallelogram or trapezoid* A line segment connecting two parallel sides of the figure and perpendicular to these two sides. Also, the length of such a line segment. Each of the two parallel sides is called a **base** of the figure.

Examples: Segment $\overline{KL}$ is an altitude of parallelogram $GHIJ$, with bases $\overline{GJ}$ and $\overline{HI}$ and segment $\overline{VW}$ is an altitude of trapezoid $RSTU$, with bases $\overline{RU}$ and $\overline{ST}$.

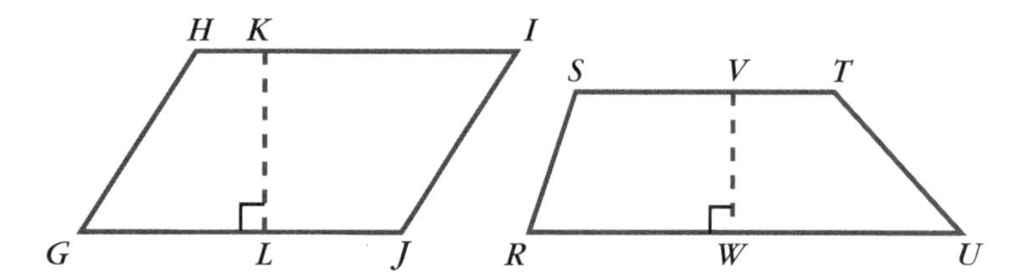

*Altitude of a triangle*

A line segment from any of the three vertices of a triangle, perpendicular to the opposite side or to an extension of that side. Also, the length of such a line segment. The side to which the perpendicular segment is drawn is called the **base** of the triangle and is often placed horizontally.

Example: Segment $\overline{AD}$ is an altitude of triangle *ABC*. Side *BC* is the base corresponding to this altitude.

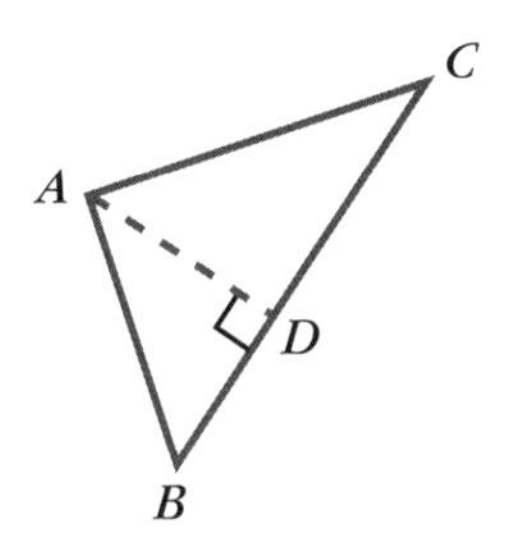


*Base*

The side of a triangle, a parallelogram, or a trapezoid to which an altitude is drawn. For **base of a prism,** see *The World of Prisms* in the unit *Do Bees Build It Best?*

*Chi-square statistic*

A number used for evaluating the statistical significance of the difference between observed data and the data that would be expected under a specific hypothesis. The chi-square ($\chi^2$) statistic is defined as a sum of terms of the form

$$\frac{(\text{observed} - \text{expected})^2}{\text{expected}}$$

with one term for each observed value.

*Composite number*

A counting number having more than two whole-number divisors.

*Cosecant*

See *A Trigonometric Summary* in *Do Bees Build It Best?*

*Cosine*

See *A Trigonometric Summary* in *Do Bees Build It Best?*

*Cotangent*

See *A Trigonometric Summary* in *Do Bees Build It Best?*

*Dependent equations*

See **system of equations.**

*Distributive property* — The mathematical principle which states that the equation $a(b + c) = ab + ac$ holds true for all numbers $a$, $b$, and $c$.

*Edge* — See **polyhedron.**

*Equivalent equations (or inequalities)* — A pair of equations (or inequalities) that have the same set of solutions.

*Equivalent expressions* — Algebraic expressions that give the same numerical value no matter what values are substituted for the variables.

Example: $3n + 6$ and $3(n + 2)$ are equivalent expressions.

*Expected number* — The value that would be expected for a particular data item if the situation perfectly fit the probabilities associated with a given hypothesis.

*Face* — See **polyhedron.**

*Factoring* — The process of writing a number or an algebraic expression as a product.

Example: The expression $4x^2 + 12x$ can be factored as the product $4x(x + 3)$.

*Feasible region* — The region consisting of all points whose coordinates satisfy a given set of constraints. A point in this set is called a **feasible point.**

*Geometric sequence* — A sequence of numbers in which each term is a fixed multiple of the previous term.

Example: The sequence 2, 6, 18, 54, . . . , in which each term is 3 times the previous term, is a geometric sequence.

*Hypothesis* — Informally, a theory about a situation or about how a certain set of data is behaving. Also, a set of assumptions used to analyze or understand a situation.

*Hypothesis testing* — The process of evaluating whether a hypothesis holds true for a given population. Hypothesis testing usually involves statistical analysis of data collected from a sample.

*Inconsistent equations* — See **system of equations.**

*Independent equations* — See **system of equations.**

*Inverse trigonometric function* — Any of six functions used to determine an angle if the value of a trigonometric function is known.

Example: For $x$ between 0 and 1, the inverse sine of $x$ (written $\sin^{-1}x$) is defined to be the angle between 0° and 90° whose sine is $x$.

*Lateral edge or face* — See *The World of Prisms* in *Do Bees Build It Best?*

*Lateral surface area* — See *The World of Prisms* in *Do Bees Build It Best?*

*Law of repeated exponentiation* — The mathematical principle which states that the equation

$$\left(A^B\right)^C = A^{BC}$$

holds true for all numbers $A$, $B$, and $C$ (as long as the expressions are defined).

*Linear equation* — For two variables, an equation whose graph is a straight line. More generally, an equation stating that two linear expressions are equal.

*Linear expression* — For a single variable $x$, an expression of the form $ax + b$, where $a$ and $b$ are any two numbers, or any expression equivalent to an expression of this form. For more than one variable, any sum of linear expressions in those variables (or an expression equivalent to such a sum).

Example: $4x - 5$ is a linear expression in one variable; $3a - 2b + 7$ is a linear expression in two variables.

*Linear function* — For functions of one variable, a function whose graph is a straight line. More generally, a function defined by a linear expression.

Example: The function $g$ defined by the equation $g(t) = 5t + 3$ is a linear function in one variable.

*Linear inequality* An inequality in which both sides of the relation are linear expressions.

Example: The inequality $2x + 3y < 5y - x + 2$ is a linear inequality.

*Linear programming* A problem-solving method that involves maximizing or minimizing a linear expression, subject to a set of constraints that are linear equations or inequalities.

*Logarithm* The power to which a given base must be raised to obtain a given numerical value.

Example: The expression $\log_2 28$ represents the solution to the equation $2^x = 28$. Here, "log" is short for *logarithm,* and the whole expression is read "log, base 2, of 28."

*Net* A two-dimensional figure that can be folded to create a three-dimensional figure.

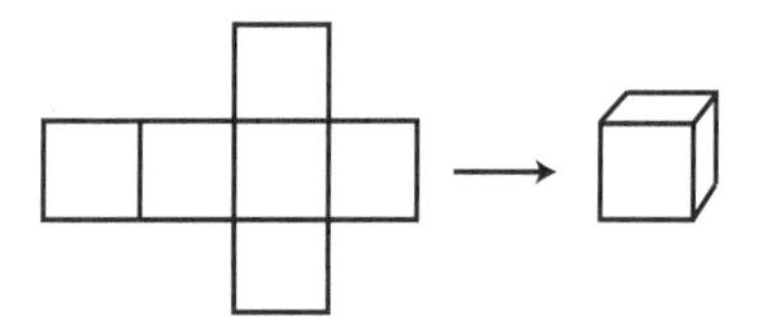

Example: The figure on the left is a net for the cube.

*Normal distribution* See *Normal Distribution and Standard Deviation Facts* in *Is There Really a Difference?*

*Null hypothesis* A "neutral" assumption of the type that researchers often adopt before collecting data for a given situation. The null hypothesis often states that there are no differences between two populations with regard to a given characteristic.

*Order of magnitude* An estimate of the size of a number based on the value of the exponent of 10 when the number is expressed in scientific notation.

Example: The number 583 is of the second order of magnitude because it is written in scientific notation as $5.83 \cdot 10^2$, using 2 as the exponent for the base 10.

*Parallelogram* A quadrilateral in which both pairs of opposite sides are parallel.

Example: Polygons *ABCD* and *EFGH* are parallelograms.

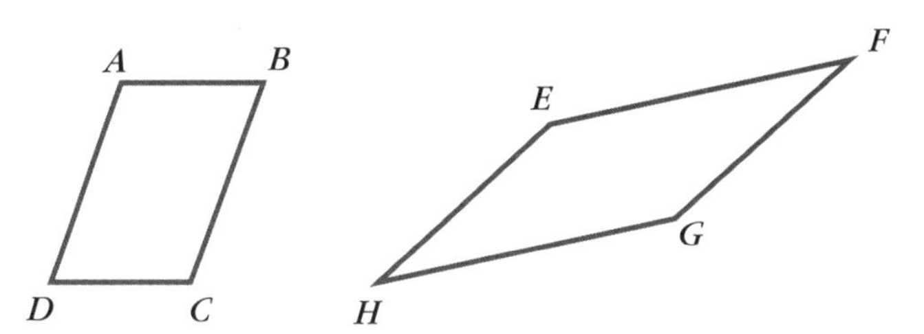


*Percentage growth* The proportional rate of increase of a quantity, usually over time, found by dividing the absolute growth in the quantity by the initial value of the quantity. Used in distinction from **absolute growth.**

*Polygon* A closed two-dimensional figure consisting of three or more line segments. The line segments that form a polygon are called its sides. The endpoints of these segments are called **vertices** (singular: **vertex**).

Examples: All the figures below are polygons.

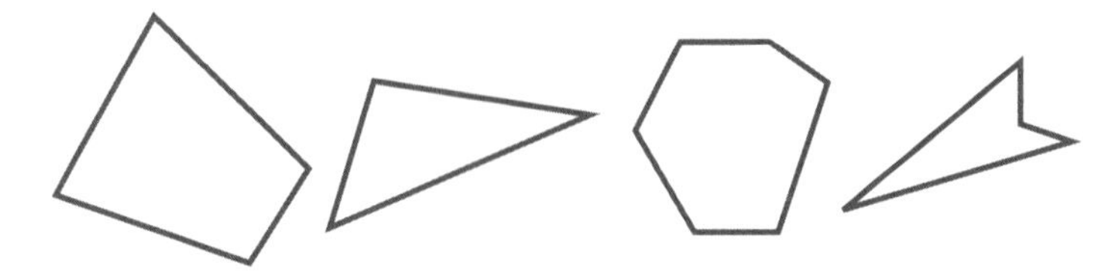

*Polyhedron* A three-dimensional figure bounded by intersecting planes. The polygonal regions formed by the intersecting planes are called the **faces** of the polyhedron, and the sides of these polygons are called the **edges** of the polyhedron. The points that are the vertices of the polygons are also **vertices** of the polyhedron.

Example: The figure below shows a polyhedron. Polygon *ABFG* is one of its faces, segment $\overline{CD}$ is one of its edges, and point *E* is one of its vertices.

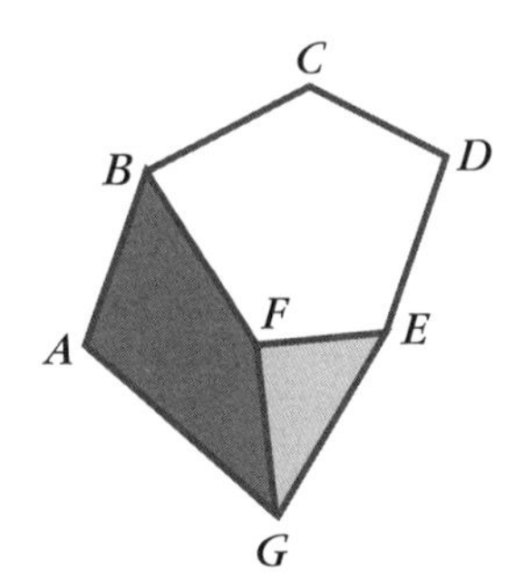

*Population* — A set (not necessarily of people) involved in a statistical study and from which a sample is drawn.

*Prime factorization* — The expression of a whole number as a product of prime factors. If exponents are used to indicate how often each prime is used, the result is called the **prime power factorization.**

Example: The prime factorization for 18 is $2 \cdot 3 \cdot 3$. The prime power factorization for 18 is $2^1 \cdot 3^2$.

*Prime number* — A counting number that has exactly two whole-number divisors, 1 and itself.

*Prism* — A type of polyhedron in which two of the faces are parallel and congruent. For details and related terminology, see *The World of Prisms* in *Do Bees Build It Best?*

*Profit line* — In the graph used for a linear programming problem, a line representing the number pairs that give a particular profit.

*Pythagorean theorem* — The principle for right triangles which states that the sum of the squares of the lengths of the two legs equals the square of length of the hypotenuse.

Example: In right triangle $ABC$ with legs of lengths $a$ and $b$ and hypotenuse of length $c$, the Pythagorean theorem states that $a^2 + b^2 = c^2$.

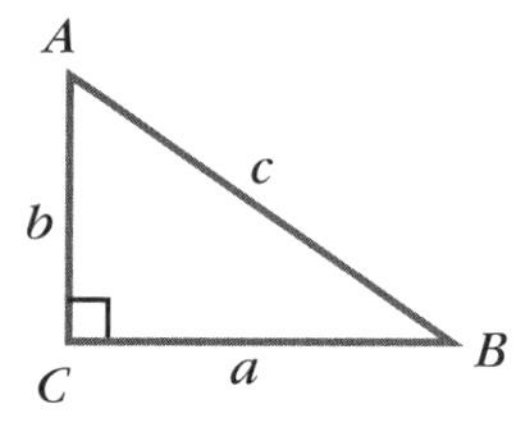


*Right rectangular prism* — See *The World of Prisms* in *Do Bees Build It Best?*

*Sample* — A selection taken from a population, often used to make conjectures about the entire population.

*Sampling fluctuation* — Variations in data for different samples from a given population that occur as a natural part of the sampling process.

*Scientific notation* — A method of writing a number as the product of a number between 1 and 10 and a power of 10.

Example: The number 3158 is written in scientific notation as $3.158 \cdot 10^3$.

*Secant* — See *A Trigonometric Summary* in *Do Bees Build It Best?*

*Sine* — See *A Trigonometric Summary* in *Do Bees Build It Best?*

*Standard deviation* — See *Normal Distribution and Standard Deviation Facts* in *Is There Really a Difference?*

*Surface area* — The amount of area that the surfaces of a three-dimensional figure contain.

*System of equations* — A set of two or more equations being considered together. If the equations have no common solution, the system is **inconsistent.** Also, if one of the equations can be removed from the system without changing the set of common solutions, that equation is **dependent** on the others, and the system as a whole is also **dependent.** If no equation is dependent on the rest, the system is **independent.**

In the case of a system of two linear equations with two variables, the system is *inconsistent* if the graphs of the two equations are distinct parallel lines, *dependent* if the graphs are the same line, and *independent* if the graphs are lines that intersect in a single point.

*Tangent* — See *A Trigonometric Summary* in *Do Bees Build It Best?*

*Tessellation* — Often, a pattern of identical shapes that fit together without overlapping.

*Trapezoid* A quadrilateral in which one pair of opposite sides is parallel and the other pair is not.

Example: Polygons *KLMN* and *PQRS* are trapezoids.

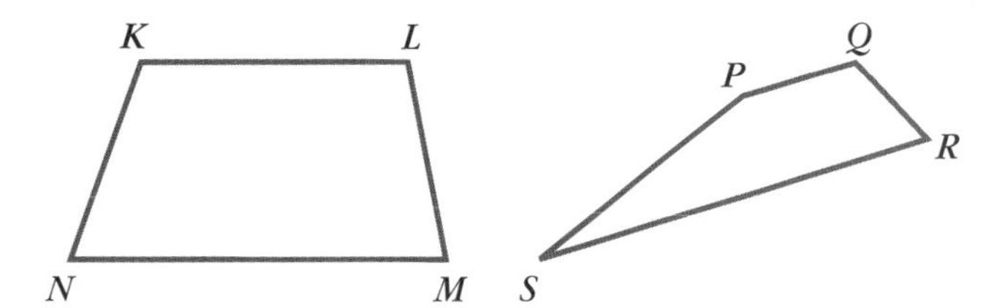


*Trigonometry* For a right triangle, the study of the relationships between the acute angles of the triangle and the lengths of the sides of the triangle. For details, see *A Trigonometric Summary* in the unit *Do Bees Build It Best?*

*Vertex* See **polygon** and **polyhedron.**

*x-intercept* A point where a graph crosses the $x$-axis. Sometimes, the $x$-coordinate of that point.

*y-intercept* A point where a graph crosses the $y$-axis. Sometimes, the $y$-coordinate of that point.

# *Photographic Credits*

## Teacher Book Classroom Photography

**26** Rosemead High School, Melody Martinez; **46** Los Altos High School, Judy Strauss, and Shasta High School, Dave Robathan; Lynne Alper; **69** Rosemead High School, Melody Martinez; **87** East Bakersfield High School, Margaret DeArmond; **124** Roosevelt High School, María Alaya-Marshall, San Lorenzo Valley High School, Dennis Cavaillé; Lynne Alper

## Student Book Interior Photography

**379** Napa High School, Steve Hansen, Lynne Alper; **382** Archive Photos; **386** Comstock © 1993; **387** San Lorenzo Valley High School, Dennis Cavaillé, Lynne Alper; **400** San Lorenzo Valley High School, Dennis Cavaillé; **412** Truman High School, Regina Schwartz, Arlene DeSimone, Lynne Alper; **419** The Image Bank; **432** The Image Bank; **433** The Image Bank; **434** Tony Stone Images; **434** The Image Bank

## Cover Photography and Cover Illustration

**Background** © Tony Stone Worldwide **Top left to bottom right** from *Alice in Wonderland* by Lewis Carroll; Hillary Turner; Hillary Turner; © Image Bank

## Front Cover Students

Colin Bjorklund, Liana Steinmetz, Sita Davis, Thea Singleton, Jenée Desmond, Jennifer Lynn Anker, Lidia Murillo, Keenzia Budd, Noel Sanchez, Seogwon Lee, Kolin Bonet (photographed by Hillary Turner)